Legend

...a true story

Legend
... a true story

LADY KITSON OBE. DL.
NEE ELIZABETH SPENCER

Edited by Carol Anderson

Forelock Books

Published by Forelock Books Ltd.

24 Lower Street, Pulborough,
West Sussex. RH20 2BL

www.forelock-books.co.uk

First published in 2016

Text Copyright © Lady Kitson OBE. DL.
Illustrations © Lady Kitson OBE. DL.

Printed in the EU by Neografia
Typeset by lksdesigns.co.uk

A CIP catalogue record for this book is available from the British Library

ISBN 978-0-9954652-0-6

In memory of Legend and for my family

Part 1
ELIZABETH'S STORY

Chapter 1

I wake up with a start hearing the roar of aeroplanes flying overhead – it is wartime. The windows rattle as they rumble over; they are very low. The room is in complete darkness, the blackout blinds down, curtains drawn. Not a chink of light must show, or the Germans would bomb. I hold my breath as another wave of planes flies over. I wait, fearing to hear the boom of the bombs. The boom comes but in the distance, probably London again. I breathe once more. Jimmy is safe.

Jimmy is my pony. He is a black Shetland pony, my playmate and friend. I spend hours in the field with him, brushing him, talking to him and also riding him bareback if my mother is not looking. Usually I get caught out because the grease from his coat makes my knickers black and oily.

It is 1941, I am three years old and we are living in Surrey. I am alone a lot as my mother does war work at a dairy farm where sometimes I play in the straw watching the milking. Some of the cows are friendly but some kick out when they are being milked. The milk goes everywhere and a lot of naughty words get shouted at them but they don't seem to care.

My father is away fighting. I don't know who my father is, by which I mean do not know what he looks like. He went away to the war when I was one year old.

Everyone is always talking about the war and people getting killed. We are often hungry. Food is short and we all have ration books. Meat, sugar, eggs and butter are some of the things that are rationed. We have some Khaki Campbell ducks that live in Jimmy's field so we have eggs and sometimes we eat a duck.

It is very cold in the house as coal is in scarce supply. It is also very dark sometimes as the blinds and curtains have to be drawn before turning on the lights. I am scared of the dark at night and I am frightened of spooks in the corners. The noise of aircraft frightens everyone, and at night you see the searchlights trying to pinpoint the planes so that the enemy ones can be shot down. Then the sound of the air raid siren makes us run and dive for the bomb shelters. We have beds and food in them because we might have to spend all night there before the 'all clear' goes up.

My mother has a horse called Piccolo and she is teaching him to pull the dogcart. He doesn't like it much as he was a point-to-point horse before the war. One day he lies down in the middle of the road while going over a bridge, pulling the cart. A policeman comes along and says, 'You can't stop here madam' and my mother says, 'Tell that to my horse, he will not get up.' They pull and haul and shout, but he won't get up. Then after what seems like an age, he simply gets up and off home we go, leaving the policeman scratching his head.

I love it when my mother sometimes straps the basket chair on to Piccolo for me to sit in and we go to see friends or go shopping. Riding is much more fun than having to walk. There is very little petrol so we only use the car on essential journeys.

One day I start thinking I could milk Jimmy like my mother did the cows, so I get a stool and a pail and sit down like my mother does, but alas Jimmy has no milk. Although I am trying very hard he doesn't seem to have the four teats the cows have. I give up and brush him instead.

It's now 1943 and we are to move down to Devon to live with Granny and Gramps and it is now that I begin to dream. Granny and Gramps, my mother's parents, live in a house on the edge of Dartmoor. They have lots of fields, a large wood by a river, and a down (which is a bit of moorland just at the back of the house). The whole place is heaven for me. We are much further from the bombs, but even now at night we can see the searchlights and hear the noise of the Plymouth air raids.

Granny is tall and thin. She talks faster than anyone you have ever heard talking. She is strict and stands no nonsense but she is also very fair. I always try to do what she tells me pretty fast. Gramps is a peppery old Admiral whom I am very scared of. He has a bad temper and when he gets very cross, he shouts and becomes red in the face. When this happens I run and hide until he has calmed down. He can also be very kind and fun. He always smokes his pipe and often he will lose it or his tobacco. I then scuttle around to see if I can find it before he does, because he is then very pleased with me.

Granny has two pony mares, Melody and Cymbal. They are sisters and live out in the fields. Melody has had a foal, which is now three years old, which my grandmother named 'Legend'. I often go into the field and watch him; he is the most wonderful mover. I am sitting up against the hedge. It is brilliant watching him gallop and leap; he trots with his head in the air and tail sticking straight up, snorting all the while. He is just like a mustang of the Wild West stories.

He tosses his head as if he is saying 'Look at me, I am the most beautiful.' He trots off as if he is moving on air. Then he gallops and stops in an instant with all his legs stuck forward. I think he is saying, 'I can do anything.'

Legend is a bright chestnut with a small white star on his forehead and a little white sock on three of his legs. When he moves in the sunlight it is like pure gold.

He was named 'Legend' because his sire (father) Lyric is the son of Mrs Muntz's famous Love Song who won at the show at Olympia before the war. He has sired many really good horses and as soon as Legend was born it was clear that he was something extra special.

Legend is still only three and not broken to be ridden. What if I could ride him one day? What if together we could win all the prizes in the horse shows? Everyone would clap and cheer as we received our rosette. He would show everybody how lovely he is and I would be with him. Sometimes I dream of winning the Grand National – winning anything and everything.

I am learning to ride so my mother has bought a grey pony from the gypsies. We have called her Granite because she is the colour of the rocks around Dartmoor. She has just arrived and I am going to ride her today for the first time. We start off down the road with my mother leading us. Granite has a hogged mane (all shaven). Suddenly she shies at something in the hedge. Ouch! I am falling forward on her neck and as my chin hits her bristly mane it feels like lots of needles being stuck into it. Quickly, I try to sit up. I just manage it and gather up my reins. On we go with me rubbing my chin.

I do hope her mane will hurry up and grow. She is

a lovely pony, very quiet but willing as well. I learn quickly and I'm soon able to ride her everywhere. (We had her for the rest of her life and she lived well into her twenties).

There is a mossy bank outside Granny's house. The moss there is very lush, thick, bright green and very soft. I call it my fairy glade. The sunlight plays through the leaves and it is a magical place to dream.

Every day I am in the field with Legend. He follows me around, curious as to what I am doing. He often nuzzles my neck, blows in my ears, which makes them tickle, and licks my hands after I give him a carrot or an apple. We are great friends. Sometimes I pick blackberries in the field and he comes to help. One day he knocks the basket over, which is very lucky for me because my mother does not find out that I have eaten far more blackberries than I have put into the basket.

Gramps grows all the fruit and vegetables for the house and we help him, picking and washing them. All the fruit that we don't eat then and there, we bottle for the winter. We also preserve eggs in a solution called china glass so that when the chickens don't lay any for a few days we still have some to eat. My uncle came to lunch today and he found a slug crawling in his lettuce, he rolled it up in the lettuce and ate it. Ugh! He said it was extra meat ration and tried to get me to do it with another one he found. I never will, but I wash the lettuce a lot more carefully now.

We pump all our drinking water from the well in the pantry. It is hard work but the water is very cold and sweet.

* * *

Now Legend is four and I am nearly five and it is time to break him in to be ridden. First, we must put a bridle on him. I think it must be strange for him having spent all his time up to now in the field. My mother starts by long reining him. I am sitting and watching, holding my breath, hoping he will do what she wants him to. First, she gets him walking and turning as she moves the reins, saying, 'walk on' or 'whoa'. When he does this well we give him lots of pats and praise. She then lunges him in a circle around her and he learns to walk, trot and canter on both reins. When she first puts the saddle on him he bucks and bucks.

I am sure he is frightened and the weight on his back is hurting him, the girth being tight and very strange. Now after a week or two he is gradually getting used to it. Next it is time for a person to lie across his back so that he can feel the weight of them on him. Little by little he is getting used to it. It is a great help that he knows and trusts us. Then the day comes when I am to get on him. I lower myself very slowly into the saddle and sit very still. Then he bucks and I am flying through the air, landing with a thump.

The grass is quite soft but my arm hurts a little. After a moment or two I get on again, and again he bucks me off. I am getting bruises. Then I manage to stay on while being led around at the walk for just a short distance. It is enough for today. For the next few days we make slow progress. He cannot bear being touched on his withers – that is to say on that bit of his neck just in front of the saddle. If I lose my balance and put my hands down at all on his withers he bucks.One night my grandmother comes to say goodnight to me as usual and then she says, 'Elizabeth, when you learn to ride Legend I will give him to you.' WOW! I am so excited I cannot sleep. I want to go and ride him now. All night I can think of nothing else. I hug myself with excitement and snuggle down in bed.

It takes a lot of time and work to get Legend to let me ride him. I plead with him but, of course, he does not understand. I must just get better. Finally, after several months I succeed and ride him round for an hour without getting bucked off.

It is my fifth birthday and I am excited. What presents will I get? My mother gives me a book on ponies and some friends come to tea and we play games. Then it is bedtime. Granny comes to say goodnight and says 'Elizabeth, I hear you rode Legend today without falling off. I am giving him to you as your birthday present.' I fling my arms round her neck. It is the best thing that has ever happened to me. 'Thank you, thank you, Granny.' Legend is mine. I have a pony of my own. I am so excited. My dream really is starting to come true.

Chapter 2

My mother and I are going for a ride and she is leading me on Legend. We are crossing a ford through a river when suddenly the leading rein gets under my leg. As Legend spooks my mother pulls the rein, which jerks my leg up and topples me out of the saddle. I am falling through the air and land in the river with a splash: it's very cold. Legend shoots forward, dragging me by my leg which has got caught in the stirrup. The ground is scraping the back of my legs and I am frightened of getting trodden on, until suddenly my leg comes free. I fall back into the river and the water goes up my nose. I come out of the river shivering and shocked. The backs of my legs hurt like crazy. It is always the rule if you fall off you get straight back on again. I am crying and frightened of getting back on, but my mother insists and anyway it is two miles home. If I don't ride I will have to walk. It is a very hot day and as we go up the very, very steep hill to the house the sun beats down on my raw and bleeding legs where my jodhpurs have been torn away. It is agony; I am desperate to get home. Finally, we get there and my legs are bathed and cream is put on.

I ride every day. Both Legend and I are improving a lot. Once a month we ride to the blacksmith's forge in the village about three miles away. I love watching the blacksmith beat out the iron by heating and shaping it, then putting it on to the foot while it's still red hot, where it sizzles on the horn. The blacksmith can then see how neatly it fits the pony's foot and he hammers it into shape on the anvil until it fits perfectly. Then he dunks it into the water trough to cool it off and very carefully nails it on to the pony's foot. He must avoid nailing it into the sensitive part of the foot, and it has to be firm enough not to fall off. I am allowed to turn the handle of the large bellows. It is very hard work and it makes my arm ache, but I must keep the fire burning. Then I can dip the shoe in the water to cool it off, being careful not to let it slip from the tongs. If it does we have to fish it out from the bottom of the trough.

We sometimes ride to the village shop or go out to lunch. Today we are going to the village so we put Granite in the pony trap and drive her there. We do our shopping. She is standing outside the post office. It's time to go but as she starts to go home she slips and falls down on her knees. She struggles up. Her knees are very badly cut and they are pouring with blood. It is horrible and must be hurting her a lot. Quick, what to do? The postmistress brings out lots of towels and we press them into the wounds. Granite is very brave and stands still. When we have stopped the bleeding, we tie the towels around the wounds and lead her very slowly home. There we can dress the wounds and bandage them properly. The vet comes and gives her an injection. It takes several weeks for her knees to heal.

*** *

One morning we wake up to find snow up to the top of the ground-floor windows. We can't open any of the doors. We have to dig our way out of the house and it takes two hours because the snow is very deep. Now we have to find and feed the ponies. Will they be all right? We dig a path to the field and then spot the ponies huddled in the shed, near the gate. We then have to get food and water to them, which takes all morning.

The snow is deeper than I am. It is well above my head and in places it has drifted to twenty feet. We can't get the car out, but after the first few days we have dug ourselves out enough to go shopping with Granite pulling us on the sledge. We take a second sledge tied on to the first one to carry the shopping. When we go to church I am often in the second sledge.

One day when going to church in this way my mother fails to tie my sledge on properly and it breaks loose as we are going up the hill. Suddenly, the sledge with me on it starts to run backwards, going faster and faster; quite fun but I scream when it runs into a huge snowdrift. I am buried in about eight feet of snow. Everyone is pulling me out and I laugh thinking that it is great fun. I am none the worse for wear, except when we get to church I am very cold.

The deep snow is very hard work. Feeding and watering our animals takes all day and we can't ride. It takes about six weeks for it to melt. Many moorland ponies, sheep and cattle died during this time because people could not find them or feed them. It has been the worst winter anyone can remember. Every day, even though our ponies live in the field, we go and brush them and check them. Also the tack, that is the saddle and bridle, has to be cleaned every time we use it. Not a job I like but it keeps it very soft and supple so it has to be done. Boring, boring!

* * *

During the last year of the war things begin to get back to normal. In the summer of 1944 there are horse shows in Horrabridge, Yelverton, Tavistock, and many other places. So I beg my grandmother and mother to let me show the ponies. They agree. There is a lot of polishing of the tack, extra grooming of the ponies till they really shine. Granite has to be washed with blue-bag to get rid of the stains on her white coat. My jodhpurs have to be scrubbed, my coat brushed and a small tie found. We will go to the shows in the dogcart with Granite pulling it. I will show Granite in the twelve two hands high class to be ridden by children under twelve years old. She is smaller than Legend, who is not yet ready to be shown.

In each class all the ponies enter the ring in single file and the judges, who are in the middle, look at us as we walk around, then trot, then canter and finally gallop. Then we slow down to a walk and the judges call us in one at a time in the order they liked the ponies best. We line up and a judge comes and looks at each pony in turn, probably asking us how old the pony is and how old we are. Then he asks each rider to go out in turn and do a show, which means you walk past the judge, then trot and canter in a figure of eight, making sure that when you canter you do so on the inside leg and strike off right each time. You can win or lose the class by one mistake as it is for the best-looking pony with the best manners. My mother comes into the ring to help me take the saddle off, as I cannot reach it on my own. The judge wants to see all the ponies with their saddles off. You stand facing the pony in front of the judge, who feels its legs for any lumps and bumps, which count against the pony. It is most important to stand the pony in exactly the correct way. Then the judge asks you to run the pony up, that is walk away from the judge, turn around and trot the pony back. It is important never to look behind at the pony and always turn by pushing the pony away from you. The judge is looking to see if the pony's legs move straight because that means that it can endure harder work. Then we all mount up again and walk around the judges, who summon us in the winning order.

The day came for our first show and I was very nervous. I lay in bed with butterflies in my stomach. Would I remember what to do? My mother shouted for me to come to breakfast but I didn't want any because I was too nervous. All the same she made me eat my bacon and eggs. I thought that I would be sick but actually food seemed to calm my nerves. Granite was spotlessly white when we finished grooming her (you always call ponies grey never white even if they are).

We set off with Granite in the trap. Legend is left behind as he is not yet ready to be ridden at the show or in the ring, and I can't ride him well enough.

Granite behaves very well and I am pulled in second. The first pony does its show and then it is my turn. Whew! All goes well. We canter on the right leg and I don't forget what to do. I get back into line. After the judge has seen Granite without her saddle we all walk around again. Once again the pony that had stood above me is pulled in first and I am pulled in second. I am very excited and pat Granite a lot. We get our rosette, which is blue for second prize. The prizewinners then canter around the ring and everyone claps. I am thrilled. Granite and I went on to win and be placed in many shows.

* * *

Now it is time for Legend's first show. I will ride him in the thirteen two hands high class for show ponies for children under fourteen years old. I am five and Legend is four. Aged five, I am the youngest rider in the class. He is a very lively and excitable character, so to get him to settle and behave properly is going to be difficult. The ponies' manes are always plaited for the shows so from early morning he knows that something is up. We arrive at the show very early and get our number from the secretary's tent. All riders wear a number either tied on to their arm or back. Then I get on him and ride him around the show ground. There are many things to surprise him such as people, dogs, tents and lots of other horses. He fusses and spooks and plays the fool. I feel quite confused. It's very difficult to pay attention to riding when there are so many things to look at. I am terrified of falling off, but gradually he gets used to all the surprises and he settles down after about an hour.

Then the loudspeaker calls all competitors for the thirteen two class to come to the collecting ring. After a final polish up, we join the other twelve ponies in the class. Legend is a fast walker so I go in first, trying to keep both him and me calm. We do it all fine. When we come back to a walk I keep an eye on the judges without seeming to do so. They called me in first, which is exciting but scary because it means that I will have to do my show first. Legend is wonderful, moving as if on air; we feel we are flying. He is enjoying showing and likes everyone to see how beautiful he is. We win the class. We canter around in front with our red rosette. My mother and Granny and Gramps are thrilled.

* * *

When we are not showing, I sometimes ride Granite on the moor with my mother or at other times with friends. Dartmoor has many bogs in which you can lose a pony, so you have to be very careful always to cross them in a safe place. I must now digress and tell you about something that happened to me some years after the time when I was showing Legend. At this time I was riding my horse called Mantle and was coming back from hunting with a friend. There was a thick fog and at about four o'clock on a winter's evening we missed the track. Suddenly Mantle was in a bog up to her neck and I was thrown on my face into it. I knew that if I tried to stand up I would be sucked down so I crawled to the edge. Mantle was firmly stuck with only her head showing. What to do? My friend Charlie said he would go for help and galloped off. I was alone and very frightened that Mantle would be sucked right under. She was tired so to start with she didn't struggle. After a while she did and I tried to pull her on to her side so that she was lying across the bog. Very slowly I made progress, but I was pulling her by the stirrups when all of a sudden they came off and disappeared into the bog, never to be seen again. But I did manage to get the saddle off. An hour had passed and it was getting dark. I was covered in bog from head to toe. I was crying and praying while shaking with cold. Would we ever be rescued?

Then suddenly Mantle gave an almighty struggle and was lying on top of the bog. She staggered up and as she did so her bridle came off in my hands. She was free but lose in a thick fog in the dark. I grabbed the saddle and bridle and followed her, pleading with her to let me catch her.

Suddenly I saw lights. The rescuers had arrived and found us. They quickly surrounded Mantle and caught her. I rode home without my stirrups, exhausted. On arrival my grandmother was furious. I suppose she had been very worried. Of course, it was before mobile telephones, eight o'clock at night and I was very late.

Another day Charlie and I were riding back from hunting and we had to cross the River Plym, in full flood between Ditsworthy Warren and Cadover Bridge. Because the river was so flooded, Charlie went first and I followed. I kicked my feet out of my stirrups as I had always been told to do, which was lucky because Mantle tripped on a boulder in the middle of the river and went down under the water. I was flung off, luckily upstream of her, so as the water swept me away I managed to grab her tail. She pulled me out as she scrambled on to the bank. My hat had come off and was swept away in the river, never to be seen again. I wonder if it bobbed around in Plymouth Sound? I was very, very lucky not to be drowned and was extremely careful about crossing flooded rivers after that. Both of these adventures occurred when I was about twelve years old. Now we must go back in time to the days after Legend's first show.

* * *

I am riding with my friends on the down, playing cowboys and Indians. We hide behind gorse bushes and jump out at each other, shouting like Indians. We also jump the gorse bushes and if the pony jinxes, or refuses, and I fall off it is very prickly; I get gorse prickles in my pants. We all often fall off but we always get straight on again even if we are hurt. We are having a great time galloping around. We just have to be careful not to arrive home with our ponies in a muck sweat, or we will be in trouble with my mother. So we cool them off and arrive back as if butter would not melt in our mouths.

Gymkhana events riding Granite are great fun. We do bending races, egg and spoon races, the sack race and many others. I have to be very quick at getting on and off. We get to know lots of the other children and their parents. Often when we have finished we watch the other classes of hacks and hunters and, of course, the jumping. The little shows are informal and fun. It is time to show Legend at county shows. He has won all the little shows so we now go to shows such as Devon County, the Royal Cornwall and the Bath and West. This means that we have to hire a horsebox. We get Eric's box, which is a cattle lorry and Eric always drives it. We have to practise loading the ponies into it. It has no partitions so we just tie the ponies next to each other, well bandaged and with their hay nets.

A county show is a big step up. My butterflies are really churning in my tummy but I must not let Legend feel them or else he will misbehave. There is a much bigger ring with many more ponies, all beautifully turned out. There are large stands with spectators all looking at us, and making a lot of noise. We now hear a band for the first time, which gets Legend very excited and causes him to dance round on his toes. I try to calm him down by talking to him and patting him as I ride him around. With all the extra ponies there is quite a crowd and I have to be careful that they do not overshadow him so the judge cannot see him. It is also important to give him enough room so that he can really show his movements. The trumpeter, who is wearing a red coat and standing in the centre of the show ring, now sounds the commands to walk, trot, canter and then gallop. We steam round and I overtake several ponies before we have to pull up. One pony won't stop; it is totally out of control. The poor girl falls off and the pony flies round loose. We all stand still until at last it is caught and led out. The girl, Anne, is OK and the judging resumes. This is serious showing and we have to do everything perfectly. Despite the disruption, Legend doesn't put a foot wrong and we win! What a wonderful feeling to be cantering around with the red rosette and the crowds clapping and cheering. Having won the class we now have to go into the pony championship for the best pony in the show. It is the biggest challenge yet.

We win the championship as well, beating all the bigger ponies and the much older riders. We win a huge silver challenge cup. We can keep the cup for one year and then it goes back to the show with Legend's and my name engraved on it, to be competed for again next year. We get a small cup to keep, and a large red, white and blue rosette.

It is now 1945. Legend is a star and we win all the shows in which we compete.

MY DREAM IS A REALITY!

After the classes have finished it's now time for some fun. We put Legend in a stable on the show ground and I change into trousers and go to look at all the sideshows, shops and displays of every sort. There are cattle, sheep and pigs being shown and I love watching the demonstrations of sheep shearing and the sheep-dog trials. In fact, I love everything to do with country life. We also go into the stand and watch the band and a motorbike display, complete with thrills and spills. It is exciting when they fall off. They run and get on again, hoping no one has noticed. The showjumping is always enthralling; they jump huge fences, which some horses go over clear. Then they jump a second round, which is the jump-off against the clock. It is very exciting and I hold my breath as they jump each fence. Will the last horse to jump win? The rider has the advantage of knowing how many fences the others have knocked down. He also knows the time he has got to beat. I sometimes stand in the collecting ring watching them warming up over the practice jump and wishing I could do it. Pat Smyth on Finality, Colonel Harry Llewellyn on Foxhunter and Colonel Mike Ansell riding Teddy were some of the showjumping heroes I admired and wanted to copy. Then it's time for the grand parade of all prizewinners from all the classes – horses, cattle, etc. Legend and I will be there as winners but it is rather boring because we just walk around rather slowly. The cattle are such slowcoaches.

Chapter 3

The war is over and my father comes home. He is tall with dark hair and a very sunburnt face because he has been in the desert; when he smiles his teeth are very white and his complexion is much darker than mine. It is very strange having him here when I have only been told about him and he isn't quite what I imagined him to be. I wonder what he thinks of me. I am nervous of him for a few weeks until we get to know each other. Life is different with three of us. It is hard to imagine all that he has been through; he never talks about what he'd been doing during the war. I am very keen to show him how well I can ride. When he can borrow a horse we spend a lot of time riding together.

**

Now we are to move to Somerset because Daddy has a job up there. I am very sad to leave my grandparents and all my friends and the wonderful riding on Dartmoor. We pack everything into boxes and then the furniture van arrives. All the furniture is put in and we wave goodbye. I am trying not to cry and sniff hard. The ponies will follow by train, but it still feels like I'm leaving them behind. About four hours later we arrive at our new home. The roads are extremely twisty, and we are very heavily loaded, so it has taken a long time. Woolston is a square red-brick house with very good stables just across the yard from the back door. It has three apple-orchard fields for the ponies to live in. I have to go to a new school. I don't like school, as reading, writing and spelling are very difficult. Everyone gets very cross with me and says that I don't try hard enough. The more I try the worse I seem to be, but no one believes me. (It was not until many years later that I was discovered as being dyslexic, so school was always difficult. Luckily I was very good at games and drawing, but very naughty and, like Legend, I was always playing the fool.)

Before I go to school every day I visit the ponies that now live in the fields close to the house. Legend always comes when called, neighing as he does so. When I get back from school in the summer I go for a ride on one of them. In the winter it is often too dark. My father now buys a horse called 'The Knight', so now we can ride together. It is not as much fun as Dartmoor because we have to ride a lot more on the roads and even though there is little traffic, we can't gallop around. We have a Jersey cow called Evelyn which we milk twice a day. Then some of the milk is put on to the cool stove in a huge flat pan and the skin that forms on the top is made into delicious Devonshire cream. We also have two white geese. We are too fond of them to eat them the first Christmas and by the second Christmas we can't catch them! So we never ate them.

Legend had won all the shows we had shown him in. Now, in 1946, he is qualified for the Royal International Horse Show at the White City in London. It is decided that we will all go by train. Legend will travel in a special horsebox on the train and we will sit in the groom's compartment to be with him. We arrive at the station in the dark. The stable goods van is waiting in a siding. We load Legend up. The steam train comes puffing up and hitches our van to it. Then with a loud whistle we are off. Puff puff chug chug. It is getting light so I look out of the window watching the fields race by. We see a fox trotting along and lots of other animals. It is great fun. The smoke billows out from the engine and the whistle goes every time we enter a tunnel. The coach sways from side to side as it rattles along. It seems to say, 'We are going to London, We are going to London, Nearly there, Nearly there.' We feed Legend and eat our sandwiches as the countryside rushes past. When we get to Waterloo Station, my father leads Legend through the streets to the mews behind the hotel where we are staying, while my mother and I take a taxi straight to the Basil Street Hotel. We meet my father and Legend as they arrive and then make Legend comfortable in the mews stables . It is exciting staying in a hotel. The food is delicious, chip potatoes and ice cream. What a treat! Yummy, yummy!

The next morning I ride Legend in Rotten Row, which is a sandy track in Hyde Park. In the afternoon my father leads him from the mews to the White City Stadium where there is a stable for him. It is a greyhound stadium but the central grass area has been turned into a show ring. One night as a treat we go to the greyhound racing. Wow, they go so fast and it's very exciting. When we arrive there I ride him around to get him used to the very strange surroundings. The next day there is the preliminary judging in the morning, then the final judging in the afternoon. This is the biggest and best show in England, so very important. Ponies had come from all parts of England – all the prizewinners and the best ponies throughout the country. I am only seven, riding against twelve-year-olds, which is quite a challenge for me.

I am very nervous. Can Legend do it? When I wake up in the morning my knees feel like jelly and my throat feels dry. I am shaking. I do not want to get up. The moment I get on Legend there is so much to think of that my nerves are forgotten. We win the class and are in the final. In the afternoon there is a huge crowd. We are milling around in the collecting ring when suddenly there is a sickening thud as one of the other ponies kicks out and catches another rider hard on the knee. She screams in pain. Everyone rushes up to help as her pony is led away and she is taken off. We are all a bit shaken but the class starts. Afterwards I hear her leg was broken. We are called in first. Legend is going like a dream, he goes perfectly. It's a brilliant show.

He is enjoying it, especially when the crowd claps and cheers. We win. Then it is time for the championship. Can my dream come true? To become champion of champions? The championship is in the evening under floodlights and we have never shown under them before; they produce shadows and I'm worried how Legend will react. Legend spooks at a practice fence in the collecting ring and I nearly fall off but I quickly regain my balance. I am called in first and the spotlight is on us as we do our show. All goes well, but will we stay first?

Yes, we win, beating all the other prize-winners in all the pony classes including the bigger ones. The spotlight is still on us. The Duke of Beaufort comes out and gives me the Rawnsley Challenge Cup. He says well done and pats Legend. He then gives me the championship rosettes and we canter around the ring in the limelight.

MY DREAM HAS COME TRUE AGAIN

Chapter 4

In the winter I go hunting with my father. The Blackmore Vale country has large thorn hedges and ditches that are exciting to ride over, but cleaning the ponies and horses afterwards is a nightmare. The thick clay mud sticks to the hair on their legs. It's best to wash the mud off and then put gamgee pads (cotton wool) on their legs and bandage them overnight, than to brush the mud off in the morning. We also have to look very carefully for blackthorns, which will poison very quickly if we don't find them that night. The horses are clipped out except for their saddle marks and legs. The Knight refuses to have his head clipped so he always looks untidy. The ponies are clipped trace high, which means not clipping the top half of them so they can be out in the field wearing New Zealand rugs. Clipping means they dry off much quicker after sweating. Sometimes the peak of my hat hits the pony's neck over the big fences and off it comes. My father gets quite cross if my hat falls off, because he has to get off to pick it up. But one day in a strong gale his top hat blows off and lands upside-down in a water-filled ditch. He puts it back on again still wet and he drips with water for the rest of the day. Very funny but he did not like me laughing at him.

We have lots of different ponies to break and school. I am always being chucked off – the most times in one day was sixteen! One of the ponies called Fantasy is very sensitive to flies. If he is in the field in the day and if the flies are biting him he will jump out of it into the road and trot around to the front gate and stand there knocking with his front hoof until someone hears him and lets him into the stable. He will stand in the stable with the door open until dark and then take himself out to the field again. Ponies are clever.

I am also doing a lot with the Pony Club on different ponies. We are split into rides and we take proficiency tests. Pony Club camp is great fun especially being in a tent. I get very scared each night by the older girls telling ghost stories. It's dark, no lights and this ghost is haunting the lane. It is a headless horseman and it's coming now. I put my head under the bedclothes and quake. Once we were ragging around and the older children put me in the water trough. I was in trouble with the instructors.

My father now starts point-to-pointing again, riding a horse called 'The Wicked Uncle', a big black horse belonging to a local farmer, Mr Clapp. We often go over to tea with the Clapps in his very old dark spooky farmhouse; his wife produces a delicious tea after my father has schooled The Wicked Uncle over the hedges around the farm ready for point-to point races. The Clapps adore the horse, to them he is one of the family. It is always so exciting watching this magnificent seventeen hands high black horse walking tall in the paddock. He so obviously loves racing. He wins or is placed in most of his races over the next two years. He won his last race and sadly died in the winners' enclosure while being unsaddled. It was awful for all of us, a terrible shock but Mr Clapp said it's a wonderful way for a horse to go, doing the thing he loved.

Years later my parents bought a horse called Airgun. My father raced him and even won a hunter-chase on him. I was allowed to ride him in ladies' races at the point-to-points. I won a lot on him and also another horse called Goldie owned by Colonel Davies. At Tweseldown, Fleet, which was my favourite racecourse,

I never lost a race there. It was very exciting jumping fences at such speed and a challenge to judge the pace to finish first, beating all the other horses. Airgun was quite a challenge. Before we had him he had injured a jockey badly coming over backwards while going down to the start. He was banned from the racecourses but not from the point-to-points. So for safety we got permission to go to the start early when he usually behaved. (I point-to-pointed for about four years; but that is another story, well in the future.)

Summer again. Now we go to many more big shows such as the New Forest, Oxford and Richmond. In fact, most of the big towns have shows. We are getting to know lots of the other competitors such as Jinks, who rides side-saddle, Ted, who is a great show-off, the Black Beetle because she has black hair and many more. We are all friends but rivals as well. Our parents always seem to want us to win. There is Jinks Skelton riding Chocolate Box or Picture Play, Ted Edgar on Debutante, Davina Lee Smith on Firefly, to name a few. Some of our parents are very fierce. We walk around the collecting ring chatting until we get caught.

One day I watch the jumping and Brian Butler's horse Tankard stops at the big wall, but the rider does not. He does a somersault over the wall ending up sitting with his back to it. The horse is one side of the wall and the rider the other. We all howl with laughter. There are often falls but very rarely does anyone hurt themselves or the horses. There are also all the show horses and riders, like Count Robert Orssich and Sam Marsh who are great riders and producers of hacks, Mrs Cooke on Knobby (a very well-known cob), David Tatlow with hunters and countless more.

Travelling to the Royal Windsor show we get delayed in the traffic and only arrive just in time. I get on Legend only ten minutes before the class is due (it usually takes at least an hour to settle him). Going into the ring I feel as if I am sitting on an unexploded bomb. The trumpeter blows to canter and we are in front of the grandstand and the judges. Legend gives a loud squeal and two enormous bucks! Luckily I manage to stay in the saddle. As I get round the ring to the exit my mother beckons me out. Legend had never been beaten before, but he definitely would have been this time for bad behaviour, had I not left the ring. I am very upset and disappointed and wish I had calmed him down. Next year we win at Windsor and I also ride a pony called Flashlight belonging to Mr Benson. He knew I had found a golden cocker spaniel puppy in one of the stalls selling dogs on the show ground, and that I desperately want a puppy. I plead with my parents without any success. Just as we are leaving the show ground Mr Benson presents me with the puppy. I am thrilled. I call him 'Windsor' and he comes everywhere with me.

Another time we leave very early to get to a show at Richmond and I am put in the back of the lorry with Legend to get some sleep. When we stop for breakfast I find that my ordinary clothes have been left behind. My mother does not want me to get my jodhpurs dirty so I nearly miss breakfast. My clothes always have to be spotless, especially if there is a best riders rosette or even a special class for best child rider in the show. I was lucky enough to win quite a few of those.

One day we are travelling to the show at Christchurch for an open pony class, that is to say a class for ponies of all different heights, and riders of any age. Professional showmen are riding some of the ponies. It is a terrible day, raining cats and dogs with a high wind. Legend and I are soaked and very miserable before we go into the ring. Legend has put his tail between his legs, his head is down and he is not at all his usual bright and bubbly self. I can hardly hold the reins my hands are so cold and the saddle soap has turned them all slimy. It is like holding a bar of wet soap. I can't see because the rain is stinging my eyes. It's horrible. We were called in sixth and that's where we stay. It is the only time he ever has anyone standing above him. All I want is to get off him, get dry and go home. I want to forget this show. The next year we win the class.

***

It's 1947, time for the White City again. A week before the show we go into the field. Legend is obviously unwell and we call the vet, who thinks he is suffering from poison. He gives him some medicine and says it is a case of nursing him and waiting for him to recover. He is very ill so we have got him in the stable all rugged and bandaged up. I am in the stable, talking to him, patting him and crying. He is lying down and very ill. It is touch and go as to whether he will recover. The vet keeps coming but he does not know what has poisoned him. After two days he begins to look a little better, standing up and eating a bran mash. It's three days to the show and he has recovered, but he has lost a lot of weight. It is worrying whether he will show himself up to his best. There is a worry that someone might have deliberately poisoned him. He always lives in the field and comes when he is called, often in the dark if we have to leave early for a show. Luckily, he did recover in time and we won again!

Chapter 5

We have to move again, this time to Rutland, the smallest county in England. The furniture van arrives. After all the furniture is put in, there is only just enough room for Legend and Puck, my new pony, to squeeze in. They are very keen not to be left behind and don't seem to mind too much. We wave goodbye to all our friends; we have a long journey to get to Rutland.

My grandmother bought Puck at a market in Devon. She bought him because he was starving and she was sorry for him. Now that he is fattened up and gelded he has become my hunter. We hunt with the Cottesmore Hunt, one of the best hunts in England. We have some wonderful runs, jumping large fences of cut and laid. These are fences where the young growth in a hedge is half cut through and then put flat on the hedge line. It makes a very good animal-proof hedge, and is great fun to jump.

During this time a very sad thing happened. Windsor was out with us as usual while we were exercising the ponies. He was normally very sensible and careful near the road but this day he ran across the road right in front of an ambulance, which could not avoid hitting him. He yelped and fell into the ditch. My father jumped off his horse, and the ambulance man went to help them both. Windsor, who was in terrible pain, bit the ambulance man in the ear as he tried to lift him. The ambulance man was bleeding badly but he said it was not Windsor's fault. He drove Windsor and my dad to the vet's before getting treated himself. Sadly Windsor could not be saved; he had internal injuries so was put to sleep. I was terribly upset, I loved that dog. It was a horrible accident.

* * *

One day at a Pony Club meet I am sent for the day to be with the master, who is also the huntsman. The hounds find a fox and go away with a great cry, with us hard on their heels. After about half an hour we get into a field from which there seems to be no way out. The huntsman says to me 'We must get through that fence.' It is a huge blackthorn bullfinch, that is to say it is twenty feet high and we have to jump through the middle. I set Puck at the fence and duck my head as we burst through. SPLASH! I am right in a duck pond. The ducks fly up squawking. The huntsman hears the kerfuffle so does not follow but shouts 'Go on Elizabeth, stay with the hounds.' I do. I am alone with the hounds, galloping and jumping everything in my path to stay with them. For over half an hour I am alone with the best hounds in England, hunting brilliantly. Then other people catch up. The fox deserves to get away and he does. We hunt him again but he is clever.

* * *

This year,1948, is a chance to win at the White City for the third time. The championship had never been won three times before. We are old hands by now but we still have to try just as hard, as there are new and very good young ponies trying to beat us. Once again the championship is ours and we win the Challenge Cup outright. FANTASTIC! No one else has ever won it three times.

Legend has won every show and as we don't want to 'pot hunt', just collect prizes, or wait till he gets too old, we are to retire him from showing. We are often asked to do a parade or do a display at some of the shows and I sometimes ride him side-saddle at these displays.

* * *

In 1949 they restarted the Olympia horse show. It had been a great horse show before the war and it is now to be called the Horse of the Year Show and to be held at the Harringay Arena in London. We bring Legend out of retirement for this one show. It is in an indoor arena. All the winners of classes throughout the year will be there to compete. We have to qualify, which we do at the county show. Can we win the championship at the huge indoor show?

Legend pulls out his very best and is brilliant, even against the younger ponies. He does a wonderful show, galloping faster than ever in a small, very brightly lit arena. We win again, the show of shows. It is the very last time he is ever shown.

As we come out of the ring Harry Llewellyn comes to congratulate me. He says to me, 'Do you want to ride a great horse.' 'Yes please,' I say and he legs me up on his famous Foxhunter, the best showjumper of the day. He lets me ride him around the collecting ring. Cantering is amazing; he is so collected and balanced that it is like being on a rocking horse. It is a wonderful experience that I will never forget. Then he puts a jump up and tells me to jump it, which I do. It's quite hard to stay on Foxhunter because he is so large compared to Legend. He puts the jump up again and we jump it several times with him putting it up each time. I had always dreamt of showjumping, having watched Pat Smythe, Alan Oliver and all the great names of the day. I had never in my wildest dreams thought I would ride one of their horses. It is so kind of Harry. I will never forget and I am hooked on showjumping from now on.

* * *

Another digression. Many years later I bought a young chestnut horse, which I showjumped. He was a very difficult horse because someone had tried to break him in before I got him and had failed. this made him frightened of everyone. It took years to get his confidence. However, I managed to get him to Grade A in two years, having won a big Grade C class at the Royal Windsor horse show and on the same day come second in the Grade B and C Championship. Grading was done on money won, so we did well to win enough to get upgraded in such a short time. We often jumped at Hickstead and were even asked to jump for the British team. Once again this is another story.

Now we reach the end of Legend's story: he truly was a legend in his lifetime. He did not really like retirement because he loved admiration and being in the limelight. He moved back to Devon and was out in the field where he injured his back so badly that he was put to sleep.

I am at boarding school as my parents are going to Malaya for three years. The headmistress tells me Legend had been put to sleep. I am so upset. I go on helping at a school tennis match with tears streaming down my face. I have lost my greatest friend and I cannot bear to think about him not being there any more. When the pain of losing him had passed I realised what a wonderful pony he was.

He had won around a hundred first prizes and championships. He had made my wildest dreams a reality. He was, indeed, a legend.

HE MADE MY DREAMS COME TRUE.
THANK YOU LEGEND!

Part 2
LEGEND'S STORY
Dedicated to my friends Granite and Flame

Chapter 1

I was born on a fine sunny day in April in a meadow in Devon. As I opened my eyes my mother was licking me and telling me to stand up and have a drink of milk. My legs were very wobbly and long; it was difficult to get them to work. At last I stood up shakily and had a drink of my mother's milk; that made me feel much stronger but I could not stand for long, so I lay down again.

I looked all around me. It was very strange, my mother was a brown pony mare, my coat was much lighter and a chestnut colour. The meadow was on a steep hill full of flowers, the birds were singing, a cow was mooing in the distance.

My mother was eating grass and encouraging me to suck her milk and get up and use my legs. She told me about all the strange noises and things around. My legs were getting stronger so now I could follow her across the field when she went to drink the water from the stream that ran through the bottom of the meadow.

Now it became colder and the sun started to disappear and it got dark. My mother stood guard and close to me to keep me warm during the night.

Each day I was getting stronger. I could now trot, canter and gallop around the meadow. While my mother was eating I could explore. I watched the rabbits as they came out early in the morning and again in the evening to feed on the grass. They ran around playing, jumping over each other; it looked great fun. I wished I had someone to play with.

The rabbits had to be very careful while they nibbled the grass; they had to keep looking out for the fox. One day the fox crept very quietly into the field; he kept very low in the grass so only his ears showed as he slunk very slowly forward through it to the nearest rabbit. Suddenly he leapt in the air and pounced on the rabbit. It let out a terrible scream then went limp; all the other rabbits bolted into their burrows while Renard the fox carried off the rabbit for his dinner and to feed his baby cubs. I was very sad for the rabbit but my mother said the fox had to eat and feed his cubs and he usually caught the silly rabbits who were not watching out properly.

Every morning a tall thin lady with short white hair came to the field. My mother said she was called Mrs Howard. When she came to the field, she called 'Melody, Melody, curp, curp' and rattled a bucket with oats in it; my mother neighed and trotted across the field to her. The first time I was rather afraid but my mother said, 'Mrs Howard owns us, she is very kind.' While my mother was eating Mrs Howard patted her and ran her hands over her body and legs, talking all the time. My mother seemed to like it and nuzzled her. Mrs Howard then turned to me and put out her hand. 'Come on little one,' she said, 'I won't hurt you.' I sniffed her hand; it was a strange smell, so I wouldn't let her touch me.

After a week I was getting used to her and I let her touch me. It felt funny at first, but after a bit I began to like it and looked forward to her coming.

I was getting braver and stronger every day. I galloped round and round my mother then down the field and up again.

One day we saw a strange horse being put in the field next door to ours; he was a bright bay and much taller than my mother. He limped over to talk to us over the hedge. He said his name was Right Royal and that he was a hunter and had come from Cornwall, where he had been owned by a man with a bad temper, who rode him very hard every day; he had hunted two days a week all season.

He told us that one day while out hunting several months ago his rider had put him at a huge fence, he had spurred him into it, hitting him with his whip shouting, 'Go on get over.' Right Royal said it was at the end of the day and he was tired. He made a great leap to jump the big fence but he could not get high enough and hit the top with his front feet, crashing to the ground on the far side. He lay winded, struggling for breath, with his leg and shoulder hurting terribly. Gradually, he was aware of people and horses gathering round, they were tending to his rider who was lying without moving. Was he dead? Someone said, 'I am a doctor, stand back.' After a while he said, 'I think he might have broken his back. We must get him to hospital, get a gate and we will carry him to the road very carefully.' Right Royal could hear all this as he struggled to breathe, then a lady came and stroked his neck and felt his legs. His near side front leg was swollen and very painful but she said, 'I don't think it is broken but the tendon is injured. Come on, old boy, can you get up.' Right Royal made a great effort and stood up, but he could hardly put his leg to the ground. The lady, whom people called Ruth, got a bandage out of a little leather case strapped to her horse's saddle and she wrapped it tight around his leg. She said, 'Come on, we have to get you to a stable.'

Right Royal hobbled very slowly and painfully to a nearby farm, he was put in a loose box with lots of straw, he was given a hot bran mash and a warm drink and his leg was bandaged again, this time with a warm kaolin poultice.

He was to remain at the farm for several weeks until he came to the field next door to us. He had heard that his rider had broken his back and was not likely to walk again and certainly not ride. So Ruth had asked if she could have Right Royal and try to get him sound again. Ruth was our Mrs Howard.

Some days later, Mrs Howard and her husband, the Admiral, came into the field. As usual, Mrs Howard put a halter on my mother, but today as she was patting me she slipped one on me. It was a shock and it felt hard behind my ears. Mrs Howard kept talking to me, saying, 'It's OK, steady Legend.' The Admiral led my mother forward, I followed my mother. Mrs Howard, who had the end of the rope of my halter, walked me around a bit; then I wanted to stop when I felt the rope tighten. I want to get it off and be free, I pulled back, I shook my head, I jumped in the air, but Mrs Howard held on, she was very strong. After a while I stood exhausted and shaking. My mother said, 'Stop fighting and follow me.' I did so and soon Mrs Howard made a great fuss of me and took the halter off. I was free again. This happened every day till I was quite used to it and could be led around without my mother. Mrs Howard now always called me 'Legend' so I realised that was my name

Then one day when we were being led around we were taken out of the gate on to the road. This led down a very steep hill, at the bottom of which we went through a gate into another meadow, our halters were taken off and we were let loose. We galloped around the field. There were some sheep feeding which when we approached them they just looked up and then went on eating.

There was a river running down one side of the field. It was wonderfully cool fresh water to drink and fun to stand in as well. On hot days we stood under the trees in the shade, swishing the flies with our tails, then we would go to the river and stand in it, pawing with our front legs to splash the water all over us. The river seemed to gurgle and chatter as it went on its way.

The sheep always stayed together; they didn't talk to us much. They were mostly ewes about to lamb. It was now that I saw the foxes again. They would sit and watch and if a ewe had twin lambs the foxes would steal the first lamb to be born while the ewe was having the second one. It was so sad, there was nothing the ewe could do. Mrs Howard realised what was happening but what to do? She could not be there all the time.

Hounds were only allowed to hunt foxes in the winter, so they could not be used to control the fox numbers. There were too many foxes and not enough rabbits and mice and other small prey for them to eat. Then Mr Snowdon, the farmer, came with his gun and he watched and waited. One of the foxes came again after several days and Mr Snowdon shot it, the bang made me jump. Over the next week he shot another fox; the lambs were not taken any more that year.

I was now beginning to eat grass; I was learning some plants tasted better than others. One day I got badly stung. I had eaten a stinging nettle by mistake. I didn't do that again.

I was standing in the river one day when suddenly a flash of silver jumped out of the water and splashed back. My mother said, 'It is a salmon returning to the river to spawn, the salmon spend the winter feeding at sea.' Now they were back in the river the salmon and sea trout were really leaping around; we would often see them; they were very beautiful, so graceful leaping high out of the water.

A few days later a little old man appeared on a bicycle, which he put against the bank inside the gate of our field. He then started to get out what my mother said was a fishing rod. He put it together and walked up the bank of the river. He had a black dog with him which he called 'Sam'. My mother and I watched him tie a fly on to his line; my mother said the fly was to catch the salmon with. He cast the fly into the water and it swam through the current until it was below him, then he cast it again gradually working down the river.

After a few hours he and Sam went home but came back the next day. The third day he was about halfway down when suddenly his rod bent double and the line went rushing out, the reel making a screaming noise. He had hooked a salmon; he spent about half an hour playing it as it tried to get free, then he quietly landed it on the bank and quickly killed it. He was delighted; he looked lovingly at it and muttered, 'This will make several meals for me and my missus, what a beauty, a great fighter.' He wrapped it up and pedalled off home. My mother said to me, 'How much nicer to be a totally free animal and have a sporting chance of getting caught or being clever enough to remain free.'

Sam was a wonderfully well-behaved dog. He sat and watched his master all the time he was fishing; then he had a share of his lunch, sitting patiently until he was thrown the scraps. The fisherman always finished with an apple; when he had eaten it, he would give me the core; it tasted delicious

One day Mrs Howard came into the field with another woman who was pushing a small fair-haired child in a pushchair. My mother and I went for the usual oats and the child held out a carrot for me. I took it, it tasted really good. Mrs Howard called the child Elizabeth; Elizabeth was Mrs Howard's granddaughter.

Chapter 2

I was quietly feeding in the field one day when a really great noise seemed to be getting nearer and nearer until a huge great shape filled the sky. I galloped to my mother; I could see she was frightened too. It flew over and the sound gradually died away. This now happened quite often but it didn't hurt us so after a while we got quite used to it.

We had eaten most of the grass in the field by the river. So the farmer came with his two very-well-trained sheepdogs to round up the sheep and take them to another field.

We were also moved back to the field I had been born in. To my delight Right Royal was in the next field again; he was looking better and said his leg was mending and he was much sounder. This time there was another horse with him. He introduced us, his name was 'Flame'. Flame had a chestnut coat much like mine but I had a white star on my forehead, while Flame had a white blaze stretching down to his nose. I had three little white socks on my legs, he had four white stockings. Flame was the Admiral's horse which he hunted and point-to-pointed.

Right Royal and Flame had just been down to the blacksmith's shop to have new shoes fitted; while they were there they heard two farmers talking about how our country, England, was now at war with Germany. They were wondering how it would affect all our lives.

Our field was on the edge of Dartmoor and the things flying overhead were aeroplanes protecting Plymouth, a big city and harbour about twelve miles away. More and more planes came over day by day and we learnt to tell the difference between bombers and fighters, English or German. We were very frightened if they were German bombers. We could see them bombing Plymouth. Sometimes they overshot the city and dropped their bombs in the country beyond or on Dartmoor. They crashed if their planes were hit coming over the coast. Everyone was very frightened at the sound of planes and went to their bomb shelters dug in their gardens or under their houses. They put water and food in the shelters, blankets and warm clothes; if there was a big raid they would spend nights or many hours in the shelters. Air raid sirens would announce a raid and would sound the all clear afterwards.

There were fears they would drop parachutists to invade Britain so everyone was looking to the skies and was very wary of strangers.

Another horse, called 'Corner Boy', now joined Right Royal and Flame in the field. He was dark brown and very grumpy and bad tempered. He wouldn't talk, and he bit and kicked if anyone went near him. He was extremely thin, his coat was dull and very dirty and he had sores all around his mouth, and raw patches where his saddle had rubbed him.

We gradually heard the story of Corner Boy. He had been owned by a very rich man from the City of London, who would come and hunt him at weekends. He was a very bad rider and pulled at Corner Boy's mouth, especially over the jumps. It hurt Corner Boy so much that he started refusing to jump; whereupon his owner laid into him with his whip until his sides were cut and bleeding. When he got back to the stable the groom was told to stop his oats and school him till he jumped properly.

The groom was sorry for Corner Boy and bathed his cuts with salt water, which stung terribly but did help them to heal. When the groom schooled him he jumped beautifully because the groom didn't jab him in the mouth. The groom could not tell the owner it was his bad riding that made Corner Boy refuse.

Corner Boy finally snapped and would not let the owner get on him; he kicked out and reared and bit him hard on the backside. Any time anyone went near him he lashed out; he trusted no one.

The owner put him in a horse sale. He was in such a sorry state that the only bid was from a knackers' man; he would be killed for horse meat. Then at the very last minute Admiral Howard, on the spur of the moment, bid ten pounds, and got him. He thought maybe if given a good home Corner Boy could be ridden safely.

During the war the Admiral joined the Home Guard and did horse patrols all around our area of the county looking for signs of trouble. All the talk was about the possible invasion of the German paratroopers.

Mrs Howard joined the Land Army helping the farmers with all the farm work. All men between the ages of eighteen and forty-one could be called up into the services to fight the war. Many of the rest of the men, especially some who were too young, volunteered and a lot went overseas. However, Britain had to feed all its people, so women and children, even the very old, all worked hard to keep the country running and to produce food to make sure there was enough to eat. They also worked in ammunition factories, which was very hard.

There was a great change at night because there was a blackout, no lights must show anywhere after dark. Because the Germans would see the lights and drop their bombs on them, not the slightest chink of light must show. So suddenly the countryside was in complete blackness, unless there was moonlight. We saw all the changes happening; it was very frightening; no one knew what would happen next.

Right Royal was now sound enough to ride, so he and Flame got to hear all this information as they were ridden from place to place. When they got back they told us all about it. They said everyone was talking in huddles in the corners. Sometimes there would be terrible news as one of the husbands, fathers, brothers or someone they knew would have been killed; there would be mourning and crying but everyone kept going and comforted each other as best they could.

Right Royal and Flame would be taken out at night on to the moor to watch for German parachutists landing as an invasion of Britain was expected. They said it was very difficult with all the granite rocks and bogs not to trip over in the dark; also it could be very cold, and was even worse if it was very wet with driving rain. They would arrive back very cold and tired. They were always given a rub-down and a hot bran mash. The starlit nights with a bright moon were quite different, very beautiful and easy to pick the way through the rocks.

After a while, Corner Boy was able to be ridden, his wounds had healed, and he realised he was with kind people. He became much happier and nicer, he stopped biting and kicking and he became friendly.

My mother and I were now joined in the field by Cymbal, my mother's sister. A bay pony mare fourteen hands high, she was a little bigger than my mother, who was thirteen two hands high. Cymbal was rather a crosspatch, she was always telling me to be quiet and not to be so clumsy, so I was determined to become an elegant pony. I would practise pointing my toes when I trotted, holding my head high and blowing out through my nostrils and arching my neck, then galloping around the field bucking and leaping in the air.

The horses in the other field encouraged me, nodding when I did well and shaking their heads when I didn't. I felt sometimes as if I was floating. I wanted everyone to admire me. I wanted to be famous.

My mother told me that when she had been four years old Mrs Howard had tried to break her in; that means teaching her to be ridden.

Because my mother was quite small, she could only be ridden by a child. The trouble was when Mrs Howard put a saddle on my mother the weight of it hurt her frightfully so she bucked and kicked to try to get it off her back. However, she could not as the girth was tight. Each day this happened and it didn't get any better. Any pressure on her withers (the part of the back where the neck joins it and the mane finishes), even if touched, was unbearable. In the end Mrs Howard had to give up and Melody would never be ridden. My mother was just unable to bear the weight of a saddle, let alone the weight of a child, on her back so she was to be a brood mare. I was her first foal.

Chapter 3

In the days we were all in the fields, the older horses would tell us the stories about their lives before the war.

Flame also told us he had been a point-to-point horse. He had been trained and ridden by Admiral Howard when he was still in the Navy, which meant he had lived in saddle club stables being looked after by a groom. Jimmy was Flame's groom, he brushed him till his coat gleamed and shone. He would be exercised for two hours a day either by the Admiral who was then a Captain or by Jimmy.

They hunted one or two days a week until the point-to-point season started. A point-to-point is a race three to four miles long across about sixteen brush fences.

There were also point-to-points over banks which they sometimes competed in; the banks were more difficult than the fly fences and could cause the most awful falls injuring both horse and rider.

Flame said he was always very careful but sometimes horses bumped into him or fell in front of him and he had to avoid treading on horse or rider. He was very proud of the fact that he had only fallen twice and each time he was brought down by another horse falling. A bank has to be jumped with the horse's feet landing on the top of it and then jumping straight off very fast.

Flame said a race was very exciting; he loved trying to beat all the other horses.

A few hours before the start time of the point-to-point races, Jimmy would ride Flame to the course. Jimmy would then rest him, brush and polish him till his coat was gleaming. Before the race he would saddle Flame up and take him to the paddock, where he would be led around with all the other horses in that race.

This is when he would see the other horses he would be racing against. He would try to work out which ones would be the danger to him and beat him. Some looked in poor condition, some looked fed up and not keen to race, some looked unhappy. Others looked very well and would be a threat as they would gallop and jump really fast.

All the people who came to the races gathered around the paddock to look at the horses; then bet their money on the horse they fancied to win.

Flame listened to the comments of the crowd as he walked around the ring and was very pleased when people said nice things about him.

Then the riders or jockeys, as they were known as, came into the ring with the horses' owners. The jockeys had jerseys of bright colours so everyone could distinguish each horse as they galloped around the course. Captain Howard was wearing his racing colours, which were red with grey hoops around the body and sleeves.

Then a bell was rung for the jockeys to mount. They were ridden to the start, where they rode up to the first fence to show the horses what they would be jumping. Then the starter got them in a line and when he dropped the red flag they all jumped off at a gallop to get a good place to jump the first fence.

One race Flame was third and they were galloping fast. He found measuring the fences fun; if he got it right he could make up ground on the horses in front. Some of the horses had fallen; there was one in front of Flame, then another passed him. When they were getting near the finish and Captain Howard was urging him on with hands and heels, Flame made a great effort to catch the two in front of him. His lungs were bursting when he came level with one of them coming up to the last fence. Flame stood right back and took a great leap; he landed in front of that horse, just one to catch now. He was gaining with every stride; could he get there before the finishing line? He made a great effort; they flashed across the line together but who had won? They pulled up covered in mud and sweat, unsure of the outcome.

Then the announcer called Flame's number out as the winner. Shouts and cheers rang out as Flame was ridden into the winners' unsaddling enclosure. The Captain got off him and went to get weighed in. All horses had to carry a certain weight in a race to make it fair.

Jimmy put a rug on Flame. There were great celebrations. Mrs Howard patted Flame and said 'well done'. People were kissing her and shaking hands. Then the Captain was presented with a large silver cup for the winner.

Flame was very excited telling us about all this. He told us about other races as well. He sometimes got beaten but he said he always did his best. However, luck played a part with horses falling and hampering him, and, of course, the condition of the ground. Flame liked it quite firm, but other horses went better on heavy ground; the condition of the ground had quite an effect on the outcome of the race.

Our field was adjacent to the moor and we would see the wild ponies over the hedge. They were rather frightened of us and people. Once a year they would be rounded up by men and women on ponies and driven into a field; there was much shouting and yelling to drive them into the right place. Their owners would then check their feet and general condition, then separate the foals from their mothers. Some would get sold the rest would be branded. (Using a red hot iron on their backs the coat would be burnt with the initials of the owner.) It must have hurt but my mother said it meant the mark would be there for ever. We felt very sorry for them but they were to live free and wild for the rest of the their lives, except for the ones selected to be sold as riding ponies or as pit ponies to go down the coal mines.

The ones that were left had a very hard time in the

winter to find enough food, and they came down into the villages to find more. To find shelter they huddled together. They would come off the moor and seek shelter between the road banks.

The war was going on and on. Food was short and rationed, so people were hungry. Almost every family had lost a member or friends in the fighting, and there were lots of wounded men without limbs and covered in bandages as they arrived back from the front line. It was a very sad time, but everyone was talking and working out how to beat the Germans.

There was an airport about six miles away on the high ground. We could see the planes landing and taking off.

One day as a plane took off there was a great crash, a flash of light and then lots of black smoke. Cymbal said, 'I think the plane hit the church tower.'

I had always heard the noise of the planes, they had been flying around since the day I was born. The other ponies had worried a great deal when they started to hear the planes but now they didn't pay much attention because they came so often. So it was a great shock to hear the awful noise of the crash, see the flash of light, then a plume of black smoke. We huddled closely together in the corner of the field, waiting to see what was going to happen next. We heard later that day Cymbal was right, the plane when taking off didn't get high enough and hit the tower of the church and cartwheeled over some houses and crashed into a field. Sadly the two pilots were killed, but the people in the church for a service were shaken but unhurt. A few days later we heard the church bell tolling for the funeral; everyone put their dark suits on to pay homage to brave men.

Every night we would see the searchlights lighting up the sky looking for enemy planes over Plymouth. One night Plymouth was bombed heavily and we could hear and see the explosions. The Admiral rode Flame down to help rescue people; he was pulling dead and wounded people out of the wreckage of their houses, everyone helped. Flame said the dust, the smell and the cries of the wounded and bereaved were terrible, he would never forget it. The whole of the centre of Plymouth was destroyed during the war. We horses could not think why all these terrible things were happening. It was four years since it had started.

* * *

I was eating one day when Mrs Howard came into the field with a little girl. I went over and Mrs Howard said, 'Elizabeth this is Legend.' Elizabeth gave me an apple and said to Mrs Howard, 'Granny can I ride Legend.' Mrs Howard said, 'You cannot ride him until he has been broken in, but we could soon start training him.'

Elizabeth clapped her hands and jumped up and down then patted me and stroked my nose. She was the baby who had given me the carrot in the meadow by the river. She and her mother came to live with the Howards; Elizabeth's father was fighting in the desert.

Chapter 4

Every day now Elizabeth would come into the field and bring me an apple or a carrot. She would talk to me and pat me; then she would wander around the field looking at flowers and butterflies. I would follow her so she would talk to me and tell me about the things she was seeing and doing. Then she would sit on a mossy bank and say she was dreaming of riding me and what we could do together.

Some days she would pick blackberries. She ate more than she put in the basket. Sometimes she would run and skip and I would follow her; it was quite a game we played. She liked it when I blew on her face through my nostrils. Elizabeth would stay in the field until Mrs Howard or her mother called her into the house.

One day she came into the field sobbing, with tears pouring down her face. She flung her arms around me and sobbed into my neck. As I nuzzled her the tears were hot and salty; gradually she calmed down. She said she had forgotten to let the chickens out and everyone was very cross with her. Then we heard them calling but she hid with me for quite a long time until Mrs Howard found her. Elizabeth said she was sorry and Mrs Howard took her in to the house. The next day she was her usual bouncy self.

Elizabeth had very pretty fair curly hair and a merry twinkle in her eyes. I think she was four years old; I was three years old.

One day a grey pony looking very scruffy and with all her mane cut off (hogged), a thick matted coat and a moth-eaten tail was put in our field. She had a kind face and came up to say hello.

She said she was a gypsy pony and she was born in a gypsy camp miles from here. She told us her mother pulled a caravan, which was all beautifully painted; the gypsies lived in it. 'Granite', as Mrs Howard called her, said she had run by her mother's side as a foal when the gypsies moved camp; which they did quite often to find more food for their ponies and to seek work for themselves.

There were eight caravans all travelling together. The gypsy men were at the war so the wives and children helped with potato or fruit picking, or any other work on the farms that needed doing. A lot of it was seasonal, which is why they moved around. In the winter they made wooden tools, clothes pegs, walking sticks, and other wooden things. They also knitted garments and cured skins to make rugs and sheepskin They made baskets of all sorts as well. They had to travel far and wide through the country to get the reeds or willows for the baskets, also to do the seasonal work.

They lived in their caravans; they washed themselves and their clothes in nearby streams. They also drank the water which sometimes made them ill, but that was if they had not collected enough rainwater to drink. They travelled England collecting and using herbs to cure illness, some people would come with their aches and pains to have themselves and their animals cured by the gypsies.

Granite's life had been fun; there were other foals to play with, until she was old enough to be broken in to be ridden and to pull the caravan. She said there were dogs, goats, chickens and sometimes even pigs all living in the camp. The cooking was done over an open fire in the centre of the campsite; if it rained all the children and animals would get covered in mud doing the chores. It was a happy life except some people didn't like the gypsies and would shout at them and try to drive them away. Some people were frightened of their healing powers.

One of the ladies was called Madge; she had a crystal ball and she would gaze into it and tell fortunes. Granite said, 'It was uncanny how often she got it right.' You had to cross her palm with silver before she would tell your fortune; sometimes she would be quite upset when she saw in her crystal ball a tragedy about to happen.

She had a heart of gold; she would help all the gypsies and really tried to help other people as well.

The children would make a lot of noise playing and mock fighting. They would sometimes do naughty things like stealing apples and poaching rabbits, food was short. This is probably what gave the gypsies a bad name.'

Granite told us she had a happy life; then one day as they were travelling to a new camp site near here, they met a man riding a very smart horse. He stopped to talk to Dave, Granite's owner. Granite said, 'The man's eyes rested on me; he came and felt my legs and ran his hands over me. He said, "I am looking for a pony for my granddaughter; is this pony well mannered and quiet to ride." Dave said, "She has the nicest temperament of any pony I have had; she is kind and willing; all the kids in the camp ride her bareback all around the place. Here Tom," he shouted at one of the boys, "show us what Granite can do." Tom rode me round and round and I did what he asked. The gentleman seemed well pleased. Then they discussed price and had a beer. When they had finished Dave came over and patted me and said, "Goodbye, be a good girl" and handed my halter rope to the gentleman, who mounted his horse and led me here.' Before Granite could say any more the Admiral and Mrs Howard came into the field with Elizabeth. Mrs Howard said to Elizabeth, 'You want to learn how to ride well so we have bought you Granite to learn on. She is quiet and well trained.' Elizabeth clapped her hands and said, 'Can we start now and will I be able to ride Legend?' The Admiral lifted her up until she was sitting astride Granite and said, 'When you have learnt to ride and know how to ride Granite, we will break Legend in and you can ride him too.' They then led her around the field on Granite.

The next day when they came into the field Elizabeth had on a new pair of jodhpurs and a smart new black-velvet riding hat. Elizabeth's mother, Mrs Spencer, was carrying a saddle and bridle, which she put on Granite; then Elizabeth was lifted on to the saddle and Mrs Spencer showed her how to hold the reins. Mrs Spencer led Granite and Mrs Howard walked beside Elizabeth, who was holding on to the front of the saddle to keep her balance. They told her to grip with her knees with her toes up and heels down. They led her around for about an hour, by the end she wasn't holding on to the saddle and could keep her balance at a walk.

They repeated the training every day. The first time Elizabeth trotted she bounced up and down and nearly fell off; it took many days before she learnt to rise to the trot. (That means go up and down as the pony trots, which is much more comfortable for both horse and rider.) Next she learnt to pull the reins to stop and to guide Granite in the direction she wanted to go. Then she was allowed off the leading rein to ride around the field.

The next stage was Mrs Spencer would ride Right Royal and lead Elizabeth on Granite and they would go for a ride round the roads or on to the moor. Elizabeth was a brave rider; she always wanted to do more and wasn't frightened of falling off, which she did quite often if Granite was startled and shied. She was always made to get straight on again so as not to lose her nerve.

I was feeling a bit left out. Elizabeth was spending more time with Granite, brushing her, riding her and cleaning her tack. Sometimes Elizabeth would be crying because she hadn't cleaned the tack well enough and had to do it again before she could come and play with me.

Chapter 5

The first time Mrs Spencer put a bridle on me, it tasted horrible; it was cold and hard in my mouth but I had seen all the other horses accept it so I put up with it. Then I had a strap put around my back and tummy. I jumped around and bucked trying to get it off but I couldn't. After this Mrs Spencer put long reins on to the bridle through the roller on my back. Mrs Howard then led me around with Mrs Spencer walking behind holding the reins; when she pulled the right one I had to turn that way, when she pulled both to stop. It wasn't too bad when I knew what to do.

Then she would lunge me (that is make me go around her in a circle at a walk trot and canter first one way and then the other). I really wanted Elizabeth to be able to ride me so I tried hard. But the first time I had the saddle on I nearly went mad; it hurt my withers so much I bucked and bucked till I was streaming with sweat and exhausted. Mrs Howard said, 'Maybe he is like his mother with very sensitive withers so perhaps we should try a sheepskin under the saddle and girth it loosely.' When they did this it was just bearable; after many weeks the muscles in my back were a little harder and it was OK.

Then one day Elizabeth was told to lie across my back. Mrs Howard held me and talked to me but I shied and Elizabeth slid off on to her feet. This went on for days. The trouble was I was very jittery and I jumped and shied before I thought. Then one day Elizabeth was legged up so she was sitting astride me and patting me. The next day she sat there and Mrs Howard said, 'Walk on.' I did but before I could stop myself I bucked, Elizabeth flew through the air and hit the ground with a thud; she cried and didn't want to get on again but she was made to. This time she stayed on. It took very many weeks before she could stay on and I learnt not to buck.

She would come into my field in the afternoons and plead with me to let her ride me. I did so want her to but it did hurt, and I was a highly strung pony and I could not control myself. She was little so she lost her balance and had to put her hands on my withers to steady herself.

Finally we both learnt and she could ride me.

* * *

She came running into my field in December, flung her arms around my neck and wouldn't let go, saying over and over again, 'Legend you are mine, you are mine, Granny has given you to me because I have learnt to ride you. It's my fifth birthday, you are my birthday present.' I was so happy I was determined to do my best for her.

Now we would go for a ride every day. Mrs Spencer would lead me from one of the horses because Elizabeth was still very small to control me. We would go down the lanes and up on to the moor.

One day we went to the blacksmith's shop in the nearby village. I was rather frightened; there was a fire burning in the forge and a smell of burning. What was going to happen? The blacksmith started by taking Granite's shoes off; he then made new ones for her by shaping red hot iron. He placed one on her hoof where it sizzled. I said to her, 'Does it not hurt and burn you?' but she said, 'No it's on the horn and it would hurt much more not to have shoes on because my feet would wear down on the roads and that would hurt.'

Then it was my turn. Elizabeth kept talking to me so I stood still and had four new shoes fitted. When the blacksmith finished and we went outside my feet felt very heavy and clumsy. After a week or two I got used to them.

One day on our way home from a ride we were crossing the ford through the river and I caught my foot on a stone on the bottom and stumbled. The leading rein somehow got under Elizabeth's leg. Her mother pulled it, it tightened it and lifted Elizabeth's leg and tipped her into the river. She fell with a splash but her foot got caught in the stirrup so before anyone realised she was being dragged through the water. Mrs Spencer shouted to stop; we did. She jumped off and picked Elizabeth out of the river. Her foot had come out of the stirrup. The water was not very deep but she was completely soaked. Also the back of one of the legs of her jodhpurs had been torn, showing her leg, which was cut and bleeding. We were a long way from home, too far for her to walk, so her mother lifted her gently on to my back and we set off. Elizabeth was in great pain and she was crying and clinging on to me and as we went up a very steep hill the sun was beating down on her raw leg. At last we got home and her mother took her into the house, and bathed the leg, which was bandaged for a week until it had healed enough for her to ride again. It had not put her off at all.

Granite used to be harnessed up to the dogcart once a week to go to the village to get food. She told me that they would take some of the surplus vegetables that the Admiral grew in the garden, and sell them or exchange them for sugar or salt or flour, some of the things they did not have.

One day Elizabeth came running into the field crying; with great sobs racking her she flung her arms around my neck. 'It's Granite; she slipped at the post office while pulling the cart and fell on her knees; they are bleeding terribly, she might die.' We saw the vet ride up. Elizabeth clung to me and I tried to nuzzle her to comfort her, but my heart was thumping, I so hoped Granite would be all right. We saw the vet ride away and Mrs Howard came and found Elizabeth and said, 'He has done what he can but she is very badly cut. However, we can keep the cuts clean and pray they will heal so she can bend her knees and the bone is not damaged.'

Granite was kept in the stable. Everyone was very worried and tried to make her as comfortable as possible. She was in great pain and could not walk and was not eating much. The horses talked to her because they went into the stables to be saddled and then ridden every day.

After a week she was making progress and would be led out twice a day. After six weeks, she made a complete recovery thank goodness, although she always had the scars of broken knees.

One day everyone was very excited, saying the war is over. The church bells were rung joyously; people had smiles on their faces. The planes stopped coming over; the searchlights in Plymouth ceased. Gradually things would change: the men started to come back from overseas; there was laughter and smiles and life became more relaxed.

We horses all talked about how it would change our lives.

Chapter 6

The horses were always kept in the stables in the winter while we ponies lived in the field whatever the season.

We had a shed we could go in to get out of the flies in the summer. They were horrible creepy crawly ones, some that really dug their legs into us and others that bit us. We would stand head to tail so we could keep the flies off each other's faces by swishing our tails. Sometimes we would gallop around to try to get away from them.

In the winter the shed kept the rain off us and sheltered us from the worst of the winds, but we were often uncomfortable even with the shed.

One afternoon it started to snow. It was very cold and it was difficult to sleep so we huddled together trying to keep warm. It snowed all night and as it became daylight we saw the snow was filling most of the doorway of the shed. We could not get out; the snow was at least six feet deep and had blown into part of the shed. We had nothing to eat and nothing to drink. We would have to wait to be rescued; we waited and waited and wondered how they would reach us. We tried eating the snow but it didn't stop us being very thirsty and extremely hungry.

The morning passed; then in the afternoon we heard voices. Gradually they got nearer. They were digging through the snow to get to us, bringing water and hay on a sledge. However, they had to dig a path to even to walk to reach us; it was even more difficult to get the sledge through the snow. When they arrived Mrs Howard said, 'It's not a lot of food and water but it's as much as we can bring today. It's starting to snow again and we have to dig everyone else out.' She was talking to the Admiral, saying that they had had to dig themselves out of the house, the snow was up to the top of the downstairs windows; they still hadn't got to the pigs to feed and water them.

It snowed again that night and also the wind blew, which piled the snow into huge drifts well over our heads. We were blocked in again; once again they brought us water and food in the afternoon.

The next day we managed to flounder down the path they had made. The trouble was we were heavy and we sank in the snow, which was up to our bellies and much higher off the track in the drifts; but we managed to get to the gate, so the food and water was brought to there. The days dragged and we tried scraping with our front legs to get down to the grass, but it was no good we could not reach it.

The water trough was frozen solid and the field by the river was too far away, we could not have been taken there. We spent the days between the gate and food, and the shed for shelter, for the next two weeks. We had snow and frost on our whiskers, making them look very funny. We were extremely cold and we talked and told stories and jokes, which helped to keep us cheerful. Our time was taken trying to find food where the wind had blown the snow away. We found patches of grass we could pick at; we also scraped every blade of hay off the ground that fell from the hay nets as we ate.

Elizabeth said she found the snow very hard as her legs were so short, and her trousers were coated in snow, but she came every day even though her nose was blue with cold and in spite of gloves her hands were icy.

After a bit, they used Granite to pull the sledge to take the food and water around to all the animals. All the lanes were blocked at first and there was nowhere to clear the snow to because of the high banks.

It took six weeks to melt but at least getting around became a bit easier. The family went shopping and to church on the sledge.

The horses we heard afterwards had had a difficult time because they could not get out of the stables and being fed corn it gave them Azoturia, which is a very painful condition where the muscles seize up in the hind quarters of the horse, and he can't walk. It needs treatment if permanent damage is not to be done.

The family went to church one day with Granite pulling the sledge with a smaller one tied on behind for Elizabeth. Granite said, 'We were going up the hill to the church when Elizabeth let out a scream, her sledge had become untied and was rushing back down the hill flat out with Elizabeth clinging to it and yelling.' Mrs Howard stopped me quickly and rushed back down the snowy road; the sledge with Elizabeth failed to go around the bend and crashed into a deep snow drift on it, Elizabeth was completely buried. Mrs Howard and Mrs Spencer got there and were able to pull her out; she was covered in snow but unhurt. We continued to church where someone wrapped her in a rug as she was shaking with cold. We got home without incident.

It was the worst winter anyone ever remembered. We heard afterwards many of the moor ponies and other animals died because no one could get to them or find them to feed or water them.

***

The summer came and there was to be a horse show in a nearby village. Elizabeth was to ride Granite so there was a great flurry of cleaning her white coat. They used blue-bag on any stains, which removed them and made her whiter; it was especially good when washing her tail. Then Mrs Spencer plaited her mane into little tight plaits all down her neck.

They then harnessed Granite to the trap to get to the show. We called good luck as they left. I don't think Granite knew what she would have to do. But Elizabeth was extremely excited and very clean and polished up. They had both been practising in the field every day.

Granite told us that night what had happened. When they got to the show, Granite was taken out of the trap and saddled up. Elizabeth then rode her around the show ground, until they were called to go into the ring with all the other ponies in the class. They had to walk, trot and then canter around the ring; they then came back to a walk. Granite said, 'They called a very pretty bay pony in first and then us; we were lined up facing the people who were watching from the side of the ring, which was marked by posts and ropes.' Then the judge came and looked at each pony in turn. She asked Elizabeth how old she was; she said 'five years old'.

Then each pony and rider had to go out one at a time to give a show. The first pony walked, trotted and then cantered a figure of eight, changing the leading leg for each circle; the bay pony's rider was ten and had done it before, they did it beautifully. Then it was Granite's turn. Elizabeth was very nervous but Granite said she knew she could do it. All went well. Granite did what Elizabeth asked and struck up on the correct leg in the middle of the figure of eight. They came back into line. The other ponies all went out one at a time; some got in a muddle, one even refused to canter.

Then everyone was told to walk around again. The bay pony was called in first and then Elizabeth and Granite were called in second. Elizabeth was thrilled to be second in her first show; they cantered around with the blue rosette fluttering from Granite's bridle.

Granite told us that night that shows were very exciting, horses and ponies of all sorts all competing; there were also jumping and gymkhana events. Lots of spectators watched the fun.

Many villages now started having shows; they were a great way of people enjoying themselves as things began to get back to normal after the war. Food was still rationed and in short supply, clothes and petrol were rationed as well so a day out nearby was important. People were working very hard to produce food and help the ill and wounded as they started to arrive home. The ill and wounded, some without limbs, had to learn how to adapt to peacetime; so many were worn out and exhausted, very tired and thin. Everyone needed cheering up.

Elizabeth and Granite were going to the shows, I was desperate to go too but I still had rather a hot temperament and jogged instead of walking if I got excited. I also could not help bucking if Elizabeth lost her balance and she would go flying. So I had to watch as they went to the shows and came back with the prizes, usually first or second.

Then one day I was taken to a show to be ridden around the show ground to see how I would behave. Granite was harnessed up to the trap and I was tied on to the back of it. When we got to the show I watched while Granite was shown. It looked fun, I was determined to behave.

When Elizabeth and Granite came out with the first prize to the cheers of everyone, it was wonderful.

Then I was saddled up and Mrs Spencer said to Elizabeth, 'Ride Legend around me in a circle.' She made us go round and round at the walk, trot and canter for a long time. At the start I felt very jumpy but after a bit I began to settle. After about an hour Mrs Spencer said, 'You can ride him round the show ground so he gets used to the people and dogs and different noises. Sit tight.' It was great fun with so much to see and Elizabeth was talking to me all the time so I was very careful to behave. We saw everything; when we got back Mrs Spencer was very pleased and said, 'At the next show you can take him into the class.'

My first show I felt very proud. I was all plaited up and my chestnut coat was glowing in the sun. Granite was in the first class for twelve two hand ponies with riders twelve years or younger. I was in the next class for thirteen two hand ponies with riders fourteen years or under. Elizabeth had ridden me around for over an hour before she showed Granite in her class, so the freshness had been worked off me. I was very excited, but very keen to show off, then I remembered Cymbal's remarks when I was a foal. So I did everything as well as possible. We were pulled in first so we had to do the first show. I did exactly what Elizabeth asked. WE WON! I felt so proud as the judge tied the red rosette on to my bridle and we cantered around the ring in front of everyone.

I knew this is what I wanted to do: always win first prize.

We went to another show; we got better and more confident as we trotted around the ring. I heard people saying 'Isn't Legend a marvellous mover, he seems to float, and his little rider is the youngest by far but she has a lovely seat, she looks part of the pony.' Elizabeth had very gentle hands on the reins; she always kept me away from ponies that might kick.

Now during the judging at the end of my individual show, we galloped once around the ring, halted, then Elizabeth reined me back four paces. My saddle was taken off and I was stood up in front of the judges by Elizabeth. I had to stand very well and still with my neck slightly arched. The judge would feel my legs and then ask Elizabeth to walk up and trot back to see if I trotted straight and my legs did not bang together.

That year, our first proper year, we won every class we went into and several championships, which were against the fourteen two hand ponies that were ridden by older children. We were the champion pony of the shows.

The next year we went to shows further away from home. Eric, who had a cattle lorry and lived across the river, would come and drive us to the more distant shows. It meant I was caught out of the field in the early morning. I always lived in the field.

In the winter the shows stopped, and hunting started.

One day Elizabeth came into the field, very excited, saying, 'My daddy is coming home today.' That evening a tall thin man with dark hair came into the field with Mrs Spencer and Elizabeth, who was jumping up and down saying, 'Daddy, Daddy this is Legend.' I went over and he patted me; he was very good looking. I could tell Elizabeth was rather shy of him at first; she had heard lots about him, but this was the first time she could remember meeting him. I had heard lots about my father too, apparently he was very good looking and was well known in top pony-circles

He was soon riding one of the horses with her every day; sometimes she would ride me and sometimes Granite. We would ride all down the lanes and on Dartmoor. Sometimes we would go out to lunch with one of their relations; it might take us a couple of hours to cover the ten to twenty miles.

Chapter 7

Elizabeth's father had been on leave since he got back from the war. Now he was given a new job in Somerset, which meant we would have to move. Everyone was very upset. Elizabeth had to leave her friends and her grandparents. I had never been anywhere else. It would mean leaving my mother Melody, Cymbal and all the other horses.

The Howards were very sad to see them go. All the furniture was packed and sent by furniture van. The Spencers had an old car; they set off in that. We were to be sent by train after they had arrived. They left and it was very quiet for several weeks.

I missed Elizabeth terribly.

Then one day Mrs Howard and the Admiral led Granite and me down to the railway station. We had our legs and tails bandaged; then we were led up a ramp into a horsebox in the railway van. I was very hesitant and needed a lot of coaxing, but after a bit I followed Granite. We were tied up next door to each other, with a partition in between, but we could see each other. We had a water trough, a manger and a hay net. The Howards said goodbye and patted us and shut the ramp. We wondered what would happen next as we started to eat our hay. Then we heard a loud noise getting nearer followed by a bump. We nearly lost our feet, the box shuddered and there was a lot of banging. Then there was a loud whistle and a lot of puffing of steam, and we started to move. We braced our legs so as not to fall over. The train gathered speed, puff, puff, puff, faster and faster; we were rattling along. After about half an hour we started to slow down and stopped. The train guard open a little door and came in; he said to the porter, 'These two seem OK.' He checked we had enough water and hay; then we were off again. After about eight stops we found our van being uncoupled from the train and pushed into a siding; we came to a stop. After a bit the ramp was put down and joy of joys there were the Spencers. Elizabeth gave us each a hug. We were very stiff and needed to stretch our legs. Then Elizabeth rode Granite and Colonel Spencer led me the six miles to our new home. We were put into an orchard full of apple trees with plenty of good grass.

Over the next few weeks we got to know our new home. The riding was very different from Dartmoor; it was mostly around the lanes, and some fields belonging to local farmers. The fields could be very wet; the soil was heavy clay, which often made my heels sore.

Colonel Spencer bought a large bay horse called 'The Knight'. As it was winter he lived in the stable and went hunting with Elizabeth and Granite. The

Knight told Granite that he had been badly treated by his last owner. He hated having his head touched and it was impossible to clip his head, so he always looked very funny going hunting as he was clipped everywhere except there. He did not like us to laugh at him.

One day Elizabeth came laughing into the field; she had been hunting the day before. Her father had often got cross if her hat fell off. But this day the wind blew his top hat off; it got blown into a ditch full of water; he swore loudly and got off in a hurry to pick it up as hounds were running and when he put it on it was full of water, which then poured down his neck!

I got rather bored in the winter as I only got ridden occasionally because Elizabeth went to school and I was too strong for her to hunt.

The next summer we started going to the shows again. The competition was stronger in Somerset and there were more shows starting up after the war. Eric came up from Devon and drove us to the bigger shows, and we went to stay in Devon to go to the big agricultural shows like the Devon County, the Royal Cornwall and the Bath and West. We saw all our friends; it was lovely.

The shows were huge; so many horses and ponies, a vast ring with showjumps to be ridden around, large stands full of people, a lot of noise, children crying, dogs barking. It was our first major show. A loudspeaker called the class numbers and we all assembled in the collecting ring. I had been ridden around for a least an hour before the class, otherwise

I would have jumped around with excitement. Elizabeth liked to get into the ring first so that I would not fuss and I could really show my paces. The ring was so big, galloping was great fun; the crowd clapped as I whizzed past. We won the class; then it was time for the championship against all the other first and second prize-winners. It was in the afternoon and there was a huge crowd; we walked, trotted, and cantered back to a walk. We won and a large red, white and blue rosette was presented to Elizabeth together with a big silver cup. It was a great thrill beating all the bigger ponies and Elizabeth at seven years old was the youngest rider by far.

After that all the prizewinners paraded, the cattle and all the winning horses; we just walked around the ring a few times. We had won at our first major show; it qualified us for the Royal International Horse Show at the White City in London much later in the year.

It was the first of many wins. Sometimes it was a lovely day, sometimes it rained; it was always exciting and we were always practising to get better. The competition was stiff, new ponies were always appearing; we had to be foot perfect.

I was plaited in the morning by Mrs Spencer; she did it very well and quickly, she never pricked me with the needle. Elizabeth always put on her jodhpurs at the show so as not to get them dirty; she wore a brownish coat and hard hat, around the edge of which her fair hair curled. She had little leather straps just below her knees to keep the jodhpurs in place. She was very small, her legs only just came below the saddle.

It was wonderful hearing all the comments at the shows. I found it hard not to boil over and made sure my manners were impeccable.

* * *

Other ponies came and lived in the next-door field, and Granite and I would talk to them over the hedge. Fantasy was a chestnut with white stockings, he had a very sensitive skin and the flies in the summer drove him mad; he would gallop around the field till he was white with sweat and in a terrible state. One day he told us, 'I am going to get into the stable.' He jumped out on to the road over a high hedge; how he did not slip up landing on the road we will never know. He then trotted down the road till he got to the double doors in the stable yard. They were open so Fantasy trotted through and into the stable. Imagine the Spencers' surprise when they found him there with the doors wide open.

After that they then took him into the stable out of the flies every day. If they were late he would jump out of the field and if the doors were shut bang on them with his front foot until he was let in. He was a very clever pony and the child who had had him before was frightened of riding and did not look after him properly, so he got naughty and did what he wanted. So he came to the Spencers to be schooled and sold on. He soon found a new home. We heard he was happy and doing a lot of hunting.

* * *

It was time for the Royal International Horse Show. We were to travel by train to London, with enough food and tack for three days. When we arrived at Waterloo Station; what a noise and bustle, it was so frightening. The Colonel was to lead me to stables for the night while Mrs Spencer and Elizabeth went in a taxi with all the kit. I had never seen so many cars on streets all lined with houses. There were hard slippery pavements; it took us about half an hour to get to the Basil Street Mews where I was to stay.

Elizabeth was there to meet me and make me comfortable, but I had never been in a stable at night. It was very difficult to sleep; it was very hot, stuffy and terribly noisy.

The horses who lived in London in the next-door stables all seemed happy and could not understand why I was worried.

The next day I was saddled up, and Elizabeth's father led me across the road to a dirt track called Rotten Row. Elizabeth rode me around for an hour or so; then the Colonel led me for an hour down the roads till we got to the White City Stadium. That afternoon Elizabeth and I did the preliminary class, which went OK; we were through to the final of the best pony class for ponies under thirteen two hands.

I was then put in a stable on the show ground for the night. It was very strange and I did not sleep well.

The next morning the class was in a huge ring in the middle of the greyhound racing track. The ring was surrounded by stands full of people. We recognised some of the other ponies because we had competed against them all year, but there were a lot of new ponies that had come from all over England. I would have to do my very best to give a perfect performance. Elizabeth was very calm although I could feel she was very nervous in case she made a mistake. She concentrated hard and kept me moving before we went into the ring. There was a trumpeter in the middle of the ring; he blew a bugle note every time we were to change from one pace to another; he looked so smart in his uniform red coat with gold braid, white breeches and black boots.

We were called in first. Elizabeth rode a beautiful figure of eight and then we galloped really fast; the crowd went mad with joy at this tiny girl on a very fast pony. She gently pulled the reins and I came back to a walk, halted in front of the judges and reined back four paces, then went back into line. When she held me out in front of the judges without my saddle, the crowd could see how very small she was at seven; the other riders could be up to fourteen years old. The spectators were captivated; I could feel them willing us on. WE Won. There was huge applause, clapping and cheers as we cantered around the ring with two rosettes. Colonel and Mrs Spencer where delighted; many people came and congratulated them; I felt very proud. The championship for all the pony classes was in the evening under spotlights. I was ridden around the ring with all the winners and seconds of the pony classes, the best ponies in England. We had to walk trot, canter and gallop, then walk around. I could feel Elizabeth glancing at the judges as we went round and round. Then the steward beckoned us in first. They only lined up the champion and reserve champion; the rest came in, in any order, behind us. The huge Rawnsley silver cup was presented to Elizabeth by the Duke of Beaufort, who said, 'Well done, it was a lovely performance' and he patted me before giving a rosette to the reserve champion, a pony called 'Tit Bit', who had been second to us in the thirteen two hand class.

Elizabeth was seven, the oldest child in the championship was sixteen; no wonder the crowd went mad as we galloped around with the spotlights on us.

It was a dream come true. I longed to tell all the other horses at home. It was better than I could have imagined when I dreamt of being famous in the field in Devon.Elizabeth won best rider in the pony classes at some of the shows we went to. We won many first prizes and were not beaten.

* * *

The field we lived in was a cider apple orchard. When the apples got ripe, we were moved out of the field because they were good to eat, a bit fizzy and sharp, but gave us a terrible tummy ache if we ate too many. They would be picked and sent in bags to be made into cider. Elizabeth was not really allowed cider, but sometimes, at the shows, when no one was looking, she would have some sips. She said it was yummy.

In the spring the fields would be covered in cowslips; they smelt lovely and were good to eat; people made them into cowslip wine.

Chapter 8

The next year we now only went to the larger shows, which meant getting up early and travelling a long way.

Going to the Richmond show; we started at five in the morning. We were in Eric's cattle lorry; Elizabeth was sleeping in the straw the other side of the partition to me. I had my hay net to eat but the Spencers wanted breakfast so they stopped. They woke Elizabeth up and then found they had forgotten her ordinary clothes. Mrs Spencer thought she would make her show clothes dirty so she nearly missed her breakfast. All was well, she got her bacon and eggs, and we won the class, another big win.

Some of the other ponies we saw at the shows were friendly and we chatted, but some were cross at being beaten and could be rude and nasty. The children who rode the nasty ponies were not kind to Elizabeth, who was young and vulnerable. I felt upset for her, but there was nothing I could do.

I remember one day we were cantering around the ring when a bay pony suddenly shot past. The little girl was shouting whoa whoa but the pony had set her jaw and was running away. The rider was hauling on the reins but the pony went on galloping faster. We all pulled up and stood still, then the pony galloped straight at the crowd. She jumped the rope at the side of the ring, knocking down five people as she went. Her rider fell off. Everyone gathered round; she was badly frightened and bruised but nothing was broken. However, one of the spectators had a broken arm and was helped away by the ambulance men. The rope was repaired and the class continued. We were rather shaken and the rumour was the pony had been stung by a bee; we never saw her again.

We had won at about ten more shows when we went to Windsor. We had a bad journey and got caught in traffic and only arrived quarter of an hour before the class. Elizabeth was crying, her parents were cross and rushing to saddle me up; the saddle was flung on and we were rushed into the ring. I was all on edge. I had not be ridden in or settled, Elizabeth was fussed. When the trumpeter blew for us to canter I completely forgot where I was. I gave a squeal and bucked twice; Elizabeth was caught completely off guard and very nearly fell off. I hoped the judges had not seen as good manners were essential for a child's pony; I had broken the rules. We were pulled in down the line. Mrs Spencer came to the exit to the ring and quietly told Elizabeth to take me out. I was so ashamed; Elizabeth got an awful ticking off and it really was not her fault. It was a sad day.

The rest of the year was going well; we had qualified for the Royal International Horse Show again. About a week before the show, one night I was in the field with Granite when we saw two men leaning over the gate talking; they called us over; they knew my name, so we thought they must be friends of the Spencers. We went over and they offered each of us an apple. While I was eating mine I thought it tasted a bit bitter but I ate it all; then the men went away.

About two hours later I got the most awful tummy ache. I walked around the field, then I laid down and rolled; but it hurt more and more and I was sweating and really ill. By the morning I was too weak to stand. Mrs Spencer and Elizabeth came to the field and found me. The vet was called immediately and said he thought I was suffering from poisoning. He tipped some medicine down my throat and gave me an injection. He said I must not be allowed to roll, so straw bales were placed around me and rugs covered me. I was in agony, but I was not left alone at all. Elizabeth or her mother or father sat with me, trying to ease the pain; the vet came back and gave me another injection. I could not stand, I was too weak, and burning up. I felt I was dying.

I heard the Spencers discussing me; they could not understand what I could have been poisoned by. Of course they did not know about the two men, but they did wonder if someone could have poisoned me so that I should not win at the Royal International Horse Show.

After twenty-four hours of terrible pain, I started to feel a little better. I could drink a little warm water then a mouthful of bran mash. It was the next day before I could stand up, five days before the show. I had lost a lot of weight, would I be strong enough to travel to the show and go well enough to win?

Elizabeth rode me in the field, I felt OK but rather weak; so it was decided to take me and see. We travelled in the cattle lorry, which was then parked in the show ground. I slept in it over night with Colonel Spencer in it as well to check I was all right. I did not feel my greatest, but I did the best I could, which was good enough to win again.

It was not as exciting as winning the first time, as it had been very worrying for everyone. This time Princess Alexandra gave me the cup, and 'Cottage Girl', the fourteen two hand winner, was reserve champion. The crowd had heard I had been ill and clapped harder than ever.

I was rested and not shown again that year. Everyone thought I had been poisoned to stop me winning; it had been touch and go. I never ate anything again given to me except by people I knew.

The horses were hunted in the early winter to qualify for the point-to-points. The country was thick clay, very heavy to gallop through, with large blackthorn hedges to be jumped. It was difficult to clean the horses' legs when they got home; but if the mud was left on the horses they would get mud fever in their heels, which I was told was extremely painful. It was difficult to cure and clear up so the horses were off work for some time if they got it badly. Also if the blackthorns in their legs were not found the same evening, by the next day the horse would have a leg like a bolster, very swollen and burning hot with poison. A kaolin poultice would be put on and hopefully that would cure it, else they would have to be put on an antibiotic to make it better.

Granite seemed to escape injury mostly, maybe living in the field helped to make her more resilient; also as a pony she had thicker hair on the heels. Granite would just have her tummy and chest clipped in the winter (a trace clip), and she lived out in the field with a New Zealand rug on. The horses lived in the stables and were clipped everywhere except their legs and saddle patch. This helped to stop them sweating too much and made it easier to clean them.

Elizabeth also took Granite to Pony Club rallies where they were taught to jump and do dressage; they competed in hunter trials, gymkhanas and other events. They were sometimes in the team competing against other Pony Clubs. There was also Pony Club camp where they spent a week camping and having riding lessons with lots of other children and ponies. Elizabeth also took tests which made her very nervous, but she always seemed to pass them; she worked very hard practising. She really enjoyed the Pony Club.

Elizabeth's mother had a baby son, whom they called Edward, Elizabeth was very excited having a baby brother, but he had a nanny who only liked babies, so Elizabeth often came by herself to talk to us in the field.

Elizabeth's mother was quite ill after the birth, so Elizabeth was kept very busy cleaning tack, brushing us off, and generally looking after us. Her mother was very strict; everything had to be done just right. Elizabeth cried when her mother was cross with her. She felt a little unwanted at times. I knew what she felt like because I suffered a bit the same in the winter when there were no shows and Granite was getting all the attention.

There were badgers that used to come through our field at night; they were looking for worms and snails. They had tracks through the field and always went the same way. They lived in a wood next door to the garden. One day Elizabeth went into one of the sheds and found one of the badgers curled up asleep. She was very excited and went to find her parents. She said the badger opened one eye and looked at her and then pretended to be asleep. When they had gone, we saw the badger come out and steal away to his holt in the woods.

Chapter 9

Spring again and we were going to the shows. Some of the little shows asked us to do a display as the champion pony in England. This was always rather fun; we would be on our own in the ring going through my paces to much applause. Elizabeth now learnt to ride me side-saddle; the crowd liked that. It was fun because there was no pressure, we could do any display we wanted.

* * *

The Spencers bought some geese there were four of them, two ganders and two females. They had quite loud voices as they talked to each other all the time and would hiss at us if we got in their way. They lived in the field during the day but were shut in at night so the fox could not eat them. I remember once watching the Spencers trying to catch the geese during the day; it was just before Christmas and the ground was hard and icy. It was so funny watching the Spencers running around; as soon as they seemed to have the geese cornered, the geese would come at them with their beaks open and give them a bite, which must of hurt. After about an hour they gave up and the geese lived with us in peace, for many years.

Evelyn the Jersey cow also lived in one of the fields. She was very calm and friendly; she never got excited except when her calf was taken away, when she would call for it for a few days. We would try to comfort her but then she would soon have another calf and she never knew what happened to the ones that left. In the summer months she would spend most of the time lying down in the grass, chewing the cud; chewing and re-chewing grass, which she said was very comforting.

She was milked twice a day and everyone liked the rich milk she gave. The Spencers made thick Devonshire cream with the milk, something they said was delicious.

We still competed at the big shows. One day we went to a show to compete in an open class against ponies shown by grownups; some very well-known riders were competing against us. It was a great coup when we beat all the professionals. At another show we got there and the heavens opened; it was pouring with rain and blowing very hard. I was very wet and cold and miserable; the rain was running into my ears, and the wind got under my tail. I could not go with my usual gaiety. The judge hardly seemed to see us and we were well down the line. It was only the second time we were beaten. I was sad but the older riders and bigger ponies did better in the heavy slippery ground and strong wind. I still shiver when I think of it.

The next time I was shown in an open class against the grown-ups, we won and beat all the ponies which had beaten us that terrible day.

At the big shows we beat all the ponies we knew well: Chocolate Box and Picture Play ridden by Jinks Skelton, Debutante and Puzzle ridden by Ted Edgar, Firefly ridden by Davina Lee Smith, Flashlight sometimes ridden by Elizabeth, the Cuffs' pony The Nut, Peter Pan, and very many more.

Elizabeth always loved watching the other classes; there were some lovely horses: hunters like Nat Galway-Greer's the Mighty Atom, the Coopers' Wavering Bee, Beau Geste, the Barretts' Moonstone; hacks like Liberty Light ridden by Count Robert Orssich; cobs like Benjamin, and Knobby ridden by Rosemary Cooke. They were superbly shown, the very best horses and riders in the country. We all displayed in the ring for the grand parade at the big shows.

Then there were the showjumpers including Foxhunter ridden by Harry Llewellyn, Colonel Mike Ansell on Teddy, Pat Smythe on Finality. They were all great combinations, jumping huge fences, which would fall if they just touched them. You had to jump clear over all the fences to get into the jump-off, and then clear again in the jump-off against the clock. It was very exciting to watch; there were many competitors in each class, some from other countries. As well as many very famous riders and their horses, there were some great characters.

Elizabeth loved going around after our class looking at all the sideshows, all the different animals if it was an agricultural show. Sometimes there was a funfair with exciting rides on bumper cars or the big dipper.

She would have an ice cream or candy floss, things she never got at home. There were so many people to talk to and we got to know the other competitors well.

One year at the Windsor horse show, after Elizabeth had ridden me in our class and won it, she was asked to ride a bigger pony called Flashlight for a Mr Benson. I was rather jealous as I felt she was my rider. They did well but didn't win their class, which left me a little relieved. Elizabeth was such a good rider she was now getting asked to ride other people's ponies but I would always be her first priority. I felt jealous again when Mr Benson presented Elizabeth with a golden cocker spaniel puppy. Elizabeth was so excited and I could see how happy she was, but my feelings were misplaced because 'Windsor', as the puppy was called, and I became good friends. Windsor went everywhere with Elizabeth; when we went riding he always came with us. He and I were the same colour so we looked good together. I did not feel left out because Elizabeth spent just as much time with me as she always had and we all three played together.

* * *

We were watching an international class at White City when one of the horses came to a big red-brick wall. The horse suddenly stopped but the rider did not; he somersaulted over the top of the wall, landing the far side, sitting with his back against it. The horse was peering over the top of the wall looking at him. The crowd was roaring with laughter.

The crowd loved all the characters, both horses and riders. There was a well-known lady rider who shouted 'hup' every time they came to a fence. There was a cob which cantered up to every fence then seemed to stop and jump from a standstill; he won quite a lot of classes. Another horse, Nizefella, would kick out when he was in the air over the fence. It was very spectacular; he never seemed to knock the fence down with his kick back.

Alan Oliver threw himself off the horse's back into the air over the fences; it lightened the weight off the horse's back but he would land on it again with quite a bang. However, it seemed to work well for him; he was very young and won a lot of classes on different horses. His placing of a horse in front of the fence was marvellous; he got it just right so the horse could jump it clear. He was a great favourite with the crowd.

The King George V Cup for men and the Queen Elizabeth Cup for women at the Royal International Horse Show were always great favourites to watch. The best horses made it look easy but others might get in quite a muddle. There were always spills and thrills as Elizabeth used to say. There was so much excitement at the shows. They were very competitive, with the best riders and horses from everywhere all wanting to win.

For the third year running we won at the Royal International Horse Show. No other pony and rider had won it three years running, before or since. I didn't know what all this meant, I was just happy for Elizabeth and I loved all the attention I was getting.

Chapter 10

The Spencers were now to move again. The furniture van was being loaded and it was getting very full. I could hear them discussing if Puck and I would be able to fit in. Puck was put in first and there was only just room for me to squeeze in, between a table and chest of drawers. It seemed like ages before we arrived at Braunston, the village that was to be our new home. We were put into a lovely big field, where we immediately had a really good roll and then went to explore.

Elizabeth was at school a lot of the time so I was to be sent back for the winter to the Howards in Devon where I was born. I was very sad and missed Elizabeth a great deal, but she came to stay with her grandmother in the holidays, and I was back in the field with my mother and Cymbal. We were happy to spend the days talking about the things we had seen and done. I had masses to tell them.

Then the summer came again and I found myself in a train travelling up to Rutland, the smallest county in England, where the Spencers were living. I was overjoyed at being back with them.

They had a nice house in Braunston. There were comfortable stables next door to the house, and they had the use of some Spencer cousins' fields. Joanna Spencer was their daughter; she was a bit older than Elizabeth but they were good friends and went riding and to Pony Club camp together. Elizabeth told me that at Pony Club camp when they were in a tent at night, Joanna told very frightening ghost stories, which really scared her.

The roads had great wide grass verges; we cantered up and down the hills on them. Almost everyone had horses and rode. The Saint, a horse the Colonel often hunted, told me, 'The hunting is some of the best in the country. Grass fields divided by cut-and-laid hedges with big ditches, they could be jumped anywhere. It was only occasionally that one had to go in single line around the headland of a ploughed field.'

When hounds found a fox the riders were able to take their own lines over the country to keep up with the hounds. They might go for ten miles or more galloping and jumping; it was very exciting. There would be many falls, sometimes horses and riders would be hurt. However, danger added to the excitement; most of the horses enjoyed hunting as much as their riders. A few did not and refused to jump; they were sold to do other work. Some of the riders would stick to the roads, which was very difficult if they owned a good horse that really wanted to gallop and jump.

Golden Morn, the Colonel's horse, told me that

good horsemen like the Colonel always got their horses fit by doing lots of road work combined with good feeding before the season started. These horses went better, and kept sounder to last out the whole season, which was October to March. They suffered less cuts and falls.

The hunters were hunted three days a fortnight; so many riders had several horses. In the summer when they were all turned out in the fields, there were horses everywhere in Rutland.Elizabeth hunted on Puck. He told us Mrs Howard had bought him in a market in Devon; he had been starved and was only two years old when she got him. He lived in the field with my mother and Cymbal; he said he got very keen on Cymbal and we heard afterwards that he fathered a foal together with Cymbal. The foal was called Gremlin.

Puck was a cheeky, confident pony, always showing off. He was bay and he had a quite ugly head, which seemed to be too big for him, but had a lot of personality, he kept me laughing. Granite was now ridden by Edward, he was smaller and lighter; this was better as she was getting quite old.

Puck thought the hunting was brilliant; lots of grass to gallop over with cut-and-laid fences. They looked very neat and were quite stiff to jump; sometimes they had a ditch in front or on the landing side.

I never went hunting for two reasons: the first because if I knocked my legs and got a swelling or a blemish it would finish my showing days; the second because I still bucked if I felt pressure on my withers so Elizabeth could never jump me much. Every time I jumped really big she lost her balance a little and put her hands on my withers; I would buck and she would often fall off. I wish I could control myself, but it was so painful, I couldn't help it, so hunting would have been impossible. Elizabeth told me that as a chestnut with a very excitable temperament she thought I would have boiled over with excitement, which would have embarrassed everyone.

I spent the winter in the field being ridden at weekends when Elizabeth was not at school. Puck now lived with me. It was nice being in the field, I could dream and remember everything we had done; also I was older and liked taking things easier. Puck and I would watch the rabbits; they had to be on watch because there was a fox that we got to know very well. He would stalk through the hedge and catch them if they were careless. Sometimes we would hear the hounds but he wouldn't worry at all unless they came very close and then he would shoot off in a bid to outwit them. He seemed to think it a challenge; he was so clever he gave them a good run and was always back the next day. He was a hunter himself so he really understood hunting. We had great respect for the way country people and animals lived their lives and respected each other.

We were quite near the church so could see a lot of life in the village. We saw people dressed in their Sunday best as if they were at a show. There was great excitement if there was a wedding and sadness if there was a funeral and watching from our field we felt very much part of life in the village. People would often come to the gate and pat us; if we were lucky we would get a carrot or an apple. Occasionally, I would hear an old person telling their grandchildren that I was a famous show pony. If Elizabeth was around she would show them the rosettes and silver cups we had won. This made me feel very proud.

The Colonel's hunters would talk to me in the summer; they never really understood why Elizabeth and I liked the shows, they thought it sounded boring. However, we all got on well together, often standing head to tail swishing the flies off each other's faces.

* * *

It was the summer again. Elizabeth and I did many demonstrations at shows; sometimes Elizabeth would ride me side-saddle. But I was only shown at the large show in Yorkshire; it was a long way to travel, but it's where we qualified for a new show, the first time it had been held after the war. The show was at Harringay Arena. It was called the Horse of the Year show and replaced the one at Olympia, which had been the show of shows before the war.

Harringay was in London and the show was in an indoor arena. It had a sawdust floor which was very dusty, so they watered and raked it in between classes. Elizabeth was nine years old now and very experienced, but I was getting old as a show pony and there were many new and young ponies to beat me. I was really retired. Could I produce the sparkle and brightness of my best?

Once again we travelled to London. The Spencers now had their own horsebox, so we went in that and then I was stabled at the Harringay Arena. The class went well and we won it. The ground was soft and dusty, the arena was quite small, the lights were bright and the crowd was very close; there was not a lot of room to gallop and the corners were sharp and slippery.

The championship was in the evening. Could I beat the bigger ponies? The lights were dazzling as we went into the ring. We did the usual walk, trot, canter and gallop. They kept us walking around a long time before calling us into the centre to line up. Then the judges told the steward to call us in first. We must do a good performance. I really tried to do a perfect show, throwing my feet out at the trot, which everyone always admired so much, cantering on the correct leg, and galloping fast without slipping up. As I watched all the other beautiful ponies do their shows I thought we can never hope to beat all of them.

Then we were called in first. We had done it again. It was the crowning glory; we had won everything we could, I was truly champion of champions.

I was pony of the year!

As we came out of the ring the showjumpers were next to go in; they were warming up for the jumping class which followed the championship. Colonel Harry Llewellyn came over to Elizabeth and congratulated her and asked her if she would like to ride Foxhunter, his Olympic horse. She replied 'Yes please', got off me, and the Colonel lifted her on to Foxhunter. She rode him around and even jumped him over a practice jump. She did it so well and looked so happy, I thought she is really ready to have a life with horses. We had achieved everything we could. We had had a wonderful time.

* * *

I was never shown again. I was retired to my field in Devon. Elizabeth went to boarding school and I saw her in the holidays. She would come to the field and talk to me of the things we had done.

All our dreams had come true; we loved each other so much.

The story of Legend, a thirteen two hand chestnut gelding, is unique. Bred by Mrs Ruth Howard and ridden by her granddaughter, Elizabeth Spencer, he won the coveted Rawnsley Challenge Cup three years running at the Royal International Horse Show. This had never been achieved before or since. Elizabeth was only seven when she won the championship for the first time.

Her adventures and successes, starting with her childhood on Dartmoor during the war, are told with humour and without conceit. Her description of travelling to London by train and on to White City, where the International Horse Show was then held, is a far cry from the luxury horseboxes of today. Her account of his suspected poisoning and getting him to recover a week before his second appearance there is harrowing. Legend must have been brave as well as beautiful. By the end of his career he had won over a hundred first prizes and championships, a true legend of his time.

Elizabeth married Frank Kitson in 1962. He was subsequently posted to Northern Ireland. This meant her sacrificing a place in the British Showjumping Team. Instead, she found consolation in painting and is now a very accomplished artist and sculptress. The watercolour sketches that accompany her story are delightful.

This is a truly fascinating account of the most famous show pony ever. Elizabeth Spencer and Legend were to showing what Harry Llewellyn and Foxhunter were to showjumping, but her story has never been told before.

Lavinia Thorpe

The Duke of Beaufort presenting Elizabeth with the
Rawnsley Cup at White City, 1946.

Elizabeth Spencer , aged 7yrs, with her pony Legend,
holding the Rawnsley Challenge Cup.

More titles from **Forelock Books:**

'**All that Glitters**' by KM Peyton

'**A Year at the Yard**' by Ken Lake

'**Finders Keepers**' by Maggie Raynor

'**One Good Turn**' by Ruth Benton-Blackmore

'**Pony Tails**' by Sue Jameson

'**Beside Me**' by Carolyn Henderson

'**Pony Racer**' by Lucy Johnson

'**Spirit and The Magic Horsebox**' by Laura Quigley

'**Spirit and The Shadow Stallion**' by Laura Quigley

'**The Horse with Big Hair**' by Sally Burrell

Visit *www.forelock-books.co.uk* for further information.